ELECTRICAL SAFETY FOR LIVE EVENTS

Marco van Beek

**ENTERTAINMENT
TECHNOLOGY PRESS**

Safety Series

ELECTRICAL SAFETY FOR LIVE EVENTS

Marco van Beek

Entertainment Technology Press

Electrical Safety
for Live Events

© Marco van Beek

First edition Published August 2004 by
Entertainment Technology Press Ltd
The Studio, High Green, Great Shelford, Cambridge CB2 5EG
Internet: www.etnow.com

ISBN 1 904031 28 5

A title within the
Entertainment Technology Press Safety Series
Series editor: John Offord

CODE / ESLE-001

FOREWORD

I am sure this reference book will be an invaluable source of guidance for everyone involved in safe electrical installations within the entertainment industry.

A few decades ago something of a cavalier attitude was often taken towards mains distribution and wiring, especially when distribution was considered a cost which could not be reclaimed on a rental, and did not appear to enhance the opinion of the audience towards the show.

The best test I can now recommend when considering whether something is safe is to ask this question: "Would you be happy for your son, daughter or loved one to work on that job or set-up, or for that matter at the top of that ladder?"

Safe installations require a sound knowledge-base and experience of what could actually happen if safety is not considered. Marco has written an excellent and easy to read book which covers this. There must never be a trade-off between safety and getting the show on the road. What is crucially important to know is what you need to do to ensure the show is safe.

Stelios Haji-Ioannou of easyJet fame said: "If you think safety is expensive, try an accident. It is infinitely more expensive." Which makes sobering reading and reinforces the fact that no accident is no accident.

Our experience at Avolites in designing and marketing mains distribution is that if approached in the right way, it will add minimal additional job costs over the life of the equipment and could even reduce costs by offering a unified and safe, reliable electrical distribution point, giving good monitoring and easy isolation when needed.

Marco's book offers an excellent single reference point and it should be compulsory reading for everyone from producer to stage-hand. For if reading this makes a safer stage, then we are all better off.

Richard Salzedo
Avolites Ltd.

CONTENTS

ACKNOWLEDGEMENTS

This book covers a dangerous subject. To make sure it was as accurate as possible, I leaned heavily on a number of other people to read assorted drafts, and to provide me with diagrams and photos: Laurence Dunnett and Gareth Winterflood of Backroom Ltd, Keith Owen of Specialz and Bill Egan of GE Energy Rentals. Any remaining mistakes are all mine.

I also owe thanks to a number of people who 'looked after me' when I was young and over-enthusiastic. They were very tolerant, and happy to impart knowledge when asked. Their patience paid off and eventually the stream of questions tailed off. I am proud to have apprenticed under them. This book is as much their knowledge as mine.

There are no such things as stupid questions, only stupid answers. So if you retain a single piece of information from this book, let it be this: "If in Doubt, Ask. And Ask, And Ask, And Ask, And Ask..."

1 INTRODUCTION

This book is aimed at all of us who have to deal with electricity in our day-to-day professional lives. Most of us have gaps in our knowledge, and you don't always know what you don't know. It starts at a basic level and progresses towards more complex issues. And please do not hesitate to put this book down when your brain gets full. The primary objective of any health and safety title should be to teach us when it is time to back off, when it is time to call someone else in. Each of us must find our own level of competence, and feel happy with where we are in the great scheme of things.

Electricity is a form of energy that is invisible to the naked eye and is present in every single object in some form or other. Every single one of us carries an electrical charge, like a battery. Sometimes we touch something (or somebody) that is at a different potential to us, and we both receive an electric shock. What we have done is to create a short circuit, and it is no different (except mathematically) from getting a shock from a faulty piece of equipment.

Because of this, an electrical hazard has little or no warning before a failure. There is often no tell-tale smell, no leaking sound, to warn people. We have to rely on protective systems rather than some sort of advance warning. The difficulty that any protective device faces is trying to distinguish between a legitimate load and a fault condition. Apart from a complete short circuit, it is very difficult to distinguish between a person and a legitimate load, other than by very careful monitoring. When you deal with dynamic loads, such as an amplifier or a dimmer, the load is so complex that this becomes a near impossible task.

So the selection of protective devices becomes a crucial task. It can literally be the difference between life and death. The conditions under which these devices

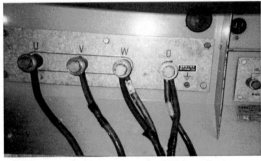

How not to do things: exposed three-phase connectors.

can operate have to be very carefully monitored, otherwise the protection will not work as intended under fault conditions – which defeats the object of having it in the first place.

But as always, prevention is better than cure, and a substantial number of problems can be spotted either by careful inspections or by sensible handling of the equipment. Modern materials are such that most equipment will succumb to mechanical damage long before normal deterioration would cause a problem.

In order for electricity to be safe, we have to place absolute reliance on two things: a sharp eye, and proper usage of protective devices.

2 TERMS USED IN THIS BOOK

In order to make this book as clear as possible, I have aimed to use the same terms throughout. However, because so many different words are used in different ways, by different people, a cross reference is provided. After each term is a collection of words that can also be used to mean the same thing.

LIVE: 'Live' refers to something that has a voltage potential above zero. It infers that the item is dangerous: live, energised.

PHASE: By using the term 'phase', we are referring to one of the three live conductors in a three-phase system.

NOMINAL VOLTAGE: In most of Europe, the national grid voltage is 230 Volts between live and neutral (400V between phases), and may vary by as much as 10% in any given situation. This 'theoretical' voltage is known as the nominal. Always know the nominal voltages of the country you are in.

NOMINAL FREQUENCY: In Europe, the nominal three-phase AC frequency is 50Hz (Hertz or cycles per second).

ISOLATED: In this book we are using the term to describe something that is *not* connected to a live conductor. It is a state where a piece of electrical equipment is safe from an external supply: dead, de-energised, disconnected.

EARTH: A mass large enough to pull any live object down to zero potential: ground.

EARTHED: Something connected to earth with a large enough conductor to be able to sink the largest fault current that may occur at that point: grounded.

GROUND: A zero voltage reference used for audio and data cabling: screen, shield, technical ground.

SUPPLY: The source of electrical power in any given situation, usually at the nominal voltage and frequency: grid, generator.

CPC: (Circuit Protective Conductor): A safety critical connection used to sink a fault to zero potential, i.e. earth, at a high enough current to operate the circuit's protective device.

PLUG: The part of a connector set that is connected to the input wire of a piece of equipment. A plug should be safe when disconnected. Can be cable or panel mounted: male, drain.

SOCKET: The part of a connector set that is connected to the supply and would normally be live. Can be panel or cable mounted: female, source.

POLE: The part of a connector that is used to connect the wires to. A pole could be live.

3 BASIC ELECTRICAL CONCEPTS

3.1 Voltage and Current

Voltage refers to the potential difference that exists between two items. They do not have to be connected to an electrical supply. The simplest analogy for electricity is water. We talk about 'feet of head' when we wonder why our shower doesn't work properly. Even though we may live in a five-storey house, the shower pressure on the top floor is the same as if we lived in a bungalow because the water is coming from a tank in the roof, 5 feet above our heads. The pressure increases the higher we can get the tank above us, and if we are on the ground floor of the block of flats, we wonder what all the fuss is about, because we have 50 feet of 'head' for our shower. Therefore a voltage can only be measured between two 'poles', and we must be aware which of those poles serves as our baseline, as our reference point. Electrical Voltage is measured in Volts.

Whenever we have a potential difference between two poles, we have the potential to produce an electric current. Electrical current is like water flow. The larger the pipe, the greater the water flow, but only if we have the pressure to 'push' it in the first place. By having a larger pipe, we reduce the 'resistance' to the flow of water. Electrical Current is measured in Amps.

3.2 Ohm's Law (R = V / I, Ohms = Volts ÷ Amps)

The relationship between resistance, current and voltage is known as Ohm's Law. The resistance, measured in Ohms is equal to the voltage divided by the current. This 'law' is fundamental to the understanding of electricity, and even when additional factors such as frequency, induction and capacitance are included, the relationship between voltage and current is maintained.

3.3 Power (P = V x I, Watts = Volts x Amps)

Electrical power is measured in Watts, and can be calculated by multiplying the voltage and current in any circuit, thus a load of 1 Ohm, if connected to a supply of 1 volt, will produce 1 Amp of current, and expend 1 Watt of energy.

See diagram over page.

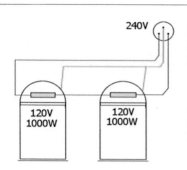

$R = V / I \therefore V = R \times I \therefore I = V / R$

$P = V \times I \therefore V = P / I \therefore I = P / V$

$P = I^2 \times R \therefore P = V^2 / R$

Circuit Current = 2000W / 240V = 8.3A

Circuit Resistance = 240V / 8.3A = 28.9Ω

Lamp Resistance = 120V / 8.3A = 14.45

These formulae only work for a snapshot of the data. In reality, the only non-variable value, the only one that cannot change, is the resistance. If the voltage changes, so will the current, and therefore the power. A 1000 Watt lamp is a nominal value based on the voltage it is supposed to be operating at. Double the voltage and, for a short time at least, it will produce double the power.

3.4 Frequency (AC versus DC)

Just when you thought it was simple, we introduce the concept of alternating current. In our water example, we were working with parallels that worked well with direct current (DC), where the electrical current flows only in one direction. This is what you get from batteries and dynamos. DC electric motors will go in one direction connected one way, and in the other when you change the wires about. Nice and simple.

So why do we need alternating current? Two reasons. The first reason is that the effects of cable resistance are more apparent at lower voltages. If you try to run cables all over the country, you are forced to use very high voltages to avoid losing too much power in the cables themselves. By using alternating current (AC) you can use transformers to change the voltage, and therefore transform up and down at will. The second reason for the change is that electrical current affects the muscles in the human body by causing them to spasm. This means that if you grasp a bare conductor at a high enough potential you cannot let go. It's nothing to do with willpower, the electrical signals your brain sends cannot compete against the national grid. However, because an alternating current supply changes direction, there are moments when the flow crosses zero, allowing you the chance to let go. At least, that's the theory…

The easiest way of generating power is by using a circular motion, so AC is produced as a sine wave. This sine wave repeats itself for every complete rotation of the shaft of the generator. This complete rotation is known as a cycle, and there are two commonly used frequencies in use in the world –

50Hz (Hertz, or cycles per second) originating in Europe, and 60Hz, from the USA, Japan, Saudi Arabia and others. Another frequency in use by the military and aviation industries is 400Hz because it reduces the size of their generators and transformers.

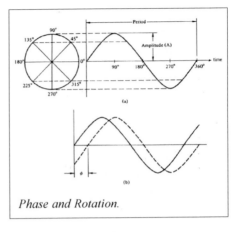

Phase and Rotation.

We also have to introduce a new way of measuring the voltage and current because otherwise, no matter what the levels were, measured over time they would average zero. The most common method, and often misinterpreted, is called RMS, or Root Mean Square (see section 10.1). This samples the waveform a number of times, and first squares each value (i.e. multiplies by itself) which changes all the values to positive. These values are then averaged (the 'mean') and the result is then square rooted. In a sine wave this value is 0.707 of the peak value (but *only* in a sine wave).

3.5 Real Power versus Apparent Power (Power Factor)

Just to confuse the issue further, when we use an AC supply, we are no longer dealing with resistance, but impedance, which can be described as the total

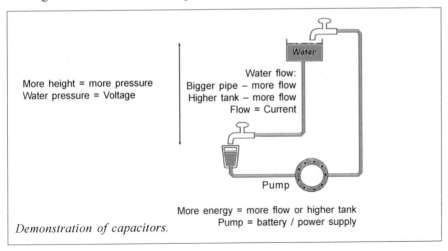

More height = more pressure
Water pressure = Voltage

Water flow:
Bigger pipe – more flow
Higher tank – more flow
Flow = Current

More energy = more flow or higher tank
Pump = battery / power supply

Demonstration of capacitors.

opposite of the flow of electricity and two new electrical concepts are introduced, the capacitor and the inductor. In very simplistic terms, the capacitor stores voltage, and its impedance (also measured in Ohms) decreases with frequency. On the other hand, the inductor stores current, and its impedance increases with frequency. When these items are introduced into a circuit, they have the strange effect of changing the normal relationship between voltage and current. The current in a purely inductive load lags behind the voltage by a quarter of the cycle, and the current in a purely capacitive load leads the voltage by a quarter of the cycle.

This bizarre effect means that power calculations have to take into account the phase angle difference between the voltage waveform and the current waveform, and in order to simplify the maths, a factor (which is the cosine of the phase difference) is used to modify the 'apparent' power, which is obtained by multiplying the RMS current by the RMS voltage, to obtain the 'real' power.

Apparent power should be expressed in 'Volt-Amperes' or VA, to differentiate it. A kVA value is often far more useful (and less misleading) than a real power figure, as it allows you to calculate your maximum current in a circuit.

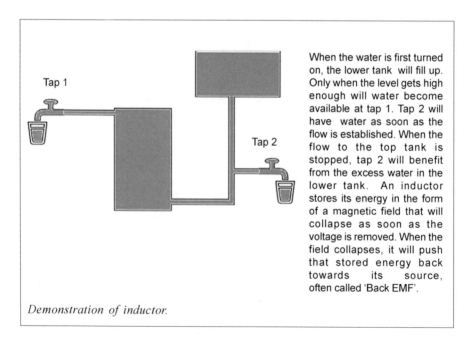

Tap 1

Tap 2

When the water is first turned on, the lower tank will fill up. Only when the level gets high enough will water become available at tap 1. Tap 2 will have water as soon as the flow is established. When the flow to the top tank is stopped, tap 2 will benefit from the excess water in the lower tank. An inductor stores its energy in the form of a magnetic field that will collapse as soon as the voltage is removed. When the field collapses, it will push that stored energy back towards its source, often called 'Back EMF'.

Demonstration of inductor.

4 BASIC ELECTRICAL SAFETY RULES

4.1 Live Work

The basic rule for live work is *Don't*. Think very carefully about this. There are no situations where readers of this book should consider live working. Trained electrical experts may have to undertake live work as part of their job but only with on-site safety precautions being in place.

4.2 Lone Working and Working in Dangerous Environments or Conditions

Never get yourself into a situation where you may be working on electrical equipment alone. This is particularly important when working in difficult situations such as outdoors or when tired.

If someone asks you to keep an eye on them, do it. It is a simple task to stay within sight of a fellow worker, and one of the simplest safe working practices around.

4.3 Isolating Circuits and 'Locking Off'

Whenever someone is working on a circuit, make sure that it is isolated, and that it cannot be connected by accident. Whether this is done by padlocks, or a simple safe working practice, is up to you but you must take steps to ensure

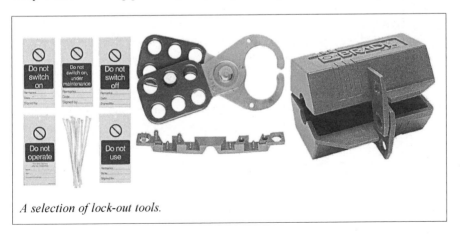

A selection of lock-out tools.

that the power cannot be connected to a circuit that someone is working on, without their consent.

Always unplug the equipment that you are working on. This is particularly important if you cannot physically 'lock off' a circuit. It may seem a little 'belt and braces', but do it so that the connector can be seen, just in case. When it comes to electricity, trust no-one, not even yourself.

There is a system that is commonly used on large industrial sites, which is called a 'Permit To Work'. This is a safe working system designed to ensure that circuits where multiple persons are working in different places without direct knowledge of each other remain safe. The person issuing the Permit To Work does not allow the circuit to be energised until all workers have 'signed off'.

4.4 Connections

Connections should always be made when a circuit is de-energised. Most connectors above 32 Amps are not rated for disconnection under load. Connecting under load is bad practice and degrades the connectors.

A selection of connectors.

4.5 Powering Up and Powering Down

Always energise and de-energise one step at a time. Never power down a system simply by turning off the main breaker, and never connect power to a circuit that doesn't require it, or isn't fully connected yet.

In order to minimise the stress on circuit breakers, which are often used and thought of as switches (which they are not, nor do they isolate a circuit as the poles are often still close enough for arcing), the smallest load should be turned off first, working back towards the main incoming supply. Energising the circuit should be the reverse, but ensuring first that all the switches and breakers are off before you start (see top diagram on facing page).

4.6 Interpretation of Test Results and Observations

Whenever you use test equipment it is important that you understand what

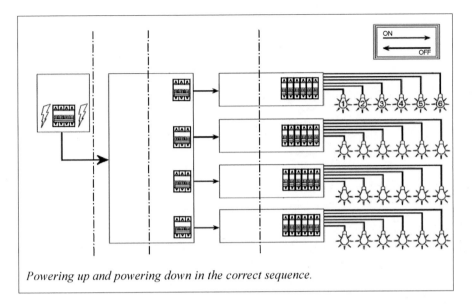

Powering up and powering down in the correct sequence.

you are looking for, as well as the limitations of the test equipment you are using. You can easily be misled by using test equipment you don't know, or by equipment connected within the circuit that may distort the results.

5 FAULT CONDITIONS

5.1 Over-Current

Over-current is a fault condition where too much current is flowing through a circuit. Left unabated, the additional heat produced may cause a failure. The current may be only slightly above the normal running current of the circuit, and therefore a protective device may not be activated, but the equipment may show signs of heat damage in specific areas, and may be hotter to the touch than expected.

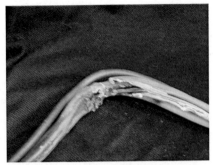

Classic symptoms of heat damage caused by overcurrent.

5.2 Over-Voltage

When a higher than normal voltage is supplied to a circuit, the additional current consumed may cause an over-current situation, but may also stress the circuit in other ways. If the over voltage is severe, (e.g. 240V instead of 120V), then wires may burn out, fuses may blow, and the insulation may be permanently damaged where it can't be seen (i.e. at cable strains).

Signs of overvoltage damage.

5.3 Under-Voltage

Under-voltage can cause problems with certain types of equipment, such as electric motors, where there may not be enough power to operate, and therefore burn out because of the current flowing though a stalled motor (where the resistance presented to the supply is at its least, and therefore allows more current to flow than normal).

5.4 Short Circuit

A short circuit is a condition where the load is bypassed completely due to a fault. This is the most catastrophic type of failure that can lead to massive damage and fire due to the immense currents that can flow. Short circuit currents are often in excess of 10,000 Amps and can lead to secondary failures in the distribution equipment (see later in the book for more information about 'breaking currents').

Melted connector caused by excessive current generating heat due to contact resistance.

5.5 Open Circuit

Open circuits can often be the hidden killer. A wire comes loose in the equipment and it ceases to work. We go over to inspect the equipment and our own fault-finding steps can cause a failure just when we are closest to it. An open circuit is a failure that disconnects at a point in the circuit. Be careful, it might not be the live wire that has broken, and it could be you that completes the circuit.

6 PROTECTION CONCEPTS

6.1 Life, Equipment and Fire

There are usually three levels of protection that can be used. The most stringent, usually only applicable to final circuits, is life protection. This means that the protective devices chosen must be aimed at preventing death. Equipment protection refers to the preventative measures that you must take to prevent damage to an individual piece of equipment.

Assorted Protection Devices.

Preventing transformers burning out due to low frequencies, avoiding damage by low (or excessive) voltages and even incorrect connections are all part of equipment protection. Fire protection is the prevention of anything that might start a fire. Electricity is capable of producing massive amounts of heat in a short space of time, so fire protection must prevent a short circuit fault condition more quickly than the cables overheat and melt.

6.2 Insulation and Conductors

The first level of protection we must look at is the rating of the cables we use. Cables are usually sized in cross-sectional area (CSA), and given in square millimetres (mm^2). Because of the way current flows in a conductor, the mathematics is not linear. A cable twice the size is not necessarily rated at twice the current. Also affecting the sums are the type of material used (e.g. copper or aluminium), the constructional method (solid or multi-strand), and the proximity to other heat sources. The numbers are all based on the temperature reached at a given current, in any given situation. As long as the cable stays below this maximum temperature (which is usually based on the materials used for the insulation), it is safe.

We also have to cover our conductors with some sort of insulating layer. This helps to prevent arcing, prevents shock, and identifies what a conductor is

being used for. Insulation is rated by the maximum (not the RMS) voltage it can stand before 'breaking down'. At this point electrons from the conductor can pass through the barrier and this can be the start of an arc. Rapid heating and a full insulation breakdown occurs and a catastrophic failure ensues. With multi-phase systems we also have to

Example of Insulation Layers.

obtain levels of insulation based on the maximum phase-to-phase voltage. Insulation materials also decay over time, which is why we have to replace building wiring.

6.3 Circuit Protective Conductor

The next level of protection we must achieve is some way of preventing a basic insulation fault from injuring a person. In most cases a piece of equipment is made of either metal or some sort of plastic. If it is metal, and a live cable touches it inside, when someone picks it up they will usually complete a circuit for the electric current to flow down, and the person will get an electric shock. So whenever we use a metal case, we 'earth' it. What that means is that we

Example of earth bonding.

connect the metal case to a Circuit Protective Conductor (CPC), which is only used to provide a better earth path than you. It is critical that the impedance of this cable is kept as low as possible, otherwise its benefits are negated. As well as reducing the effects of an electric shock, the CPC (referred to as Earth or sometimes Ground) should help to cause a fault condition, which will cause the protective device on the circuit to disconnect the current. If we get a blown fuse on a piece of equipment, we should inspect it carefully before simply powering it up again.

6.4 Isolation of Live Circuits

There are two different uses of the term 'isolation', which can cause much confusion. The first refers to a 'safe' state of a circuit which is isolated by disconnection from the supply. An isolating switch (or Isolator) not only disconnects the supply (and can often be locked off), but physically separates the two sides of the switch by a distance sufficient to prevent any possibility of any current flowing in the circuit under any circumstances. It is therefore, as far as any electrical safety requirement is concerned, as safe as if you have unplugged it.

Example of a lock-out device.

The best isolation of a circuit is to unplug it where you can see it, even if the other end is locked.

See section 6.8 for further definitions of isolation.

6.5 Earth Loop Impedance (and the Effect of Cable Lengths)

Because of the crucial nature of the CPC, it is imperative that we understand the concept of 'Earth Loop Impedance'. Earth Loop Impedance is the impedance in the case of a dead short at the furthest point from the protective device. All over-current protective devices need a period of time in which to react. The higher the over-current, the quicker the device reacts. Below a certain point, the protective device will not operate, and even just above that point may take hours to reach the tripping point.

If we assume a piece of equipment has a fault whereby the live cable comes adrift and shorts to the casing, then the total load on the circuit becomes the impedance of the cable up to, and back down from, the equipment. This is known as the Earth Loop Impedance. The higher this is, the lower the total fault current. When we look at the fault current versus the tripping time graph of our protective device, and if following the best advice available to us (the IEE), we must achieve a tripping time of no more than 0.4s, which will give us a minimum fault current allowed to flow in the circuit. If we cannot achieve this we must do one of two things: improve our cabling (by reducing the length or increasing the CSA) or improve our protective device.

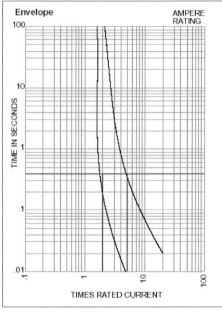

6.6 Equipotential Bonding

Equipotential Bonding, as the name implies, is a method used to ensure that all metalwork is at the same potential, i.e. ground. Whenever we are in a situation where we can touch two pieces of metal at the same time, where one may become live, we must ensure that they are both at the same potential, so that you cannot get an electric shock between the two.

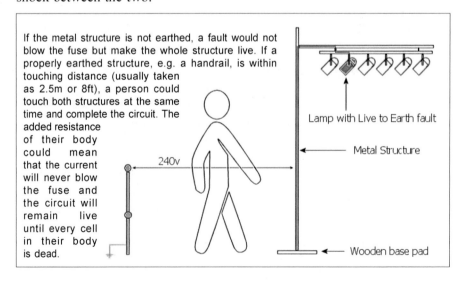

If the metal structure is not earthed, a fault would not blow the fuse but make the whole structure live. If a properly earthed structure, e.g. a handrail, is within touching distance (usually taken as 2.5m or 8ft), a person could touch both structures at the same time and complete the circuit. The added resistance of their body could mean that the current will never blow the fuse and the circuit will remain live until every cell in their body is dead.

240v

Lamp with Live to Earth fault

Metal Structure

Wooden base pad

An example of this is a scaffolding-based lighting tower, where if an electric cable were damaged, and the live cable were touching the scaffolding, the fault would remain undetected until someone or something made a connection between the scaffolding and something that provides a path to earth. At this point, and only at this point, would any protective devices come into play.

What is important to remember is that the fault, and the point of shock, could be a substantial distance from one another, as well as the normal assumption that the piece of equipment that completed the circuit was at fault.

6.7 Residual Current

Residual current is the current that would be missing if you measured the current flowing up the live conductor and subtracted the current coming back down the neutral. It is getting 'lost' somewhere along the way, either by induction, capacitive effect, directed to earth by a filter circuit, or even due to damp in a connector somewhere. Some residual current is to be expected, especially considering the increased use of switched mode power supplies and the massive amount of noise filtering they must now have due to the Electro Magnetic Compatibility directive.

What also happens is that most filters have capacitors between live, neutral and earth which, when the supply is turned on, have to charge and this creates an imbalance that is interpreted as a fault by the RCD, which shuts down the circuit.

It has been suggested that it would not be unusual to expect 1 milliAmp of leakage current per KiloWatt. This equates to 1 Amp of leakage per MegaWatt, so a 30mA trip on a 400Amp supply is more likely to get triggered by background leakage than a real fault.

It is very important to make the distinction between a background level of residual current and a fault condition. It may be perfectly normal to expect a large lighting system to have a background residual current in excess of 100mA,

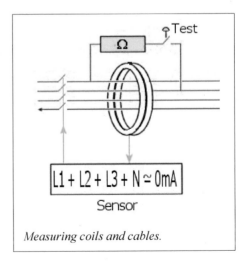

Measuring coils and cables.

and for nothing to be wrong. However, when we use Residual Current Devices, we are often required to use ones rated at 30mA because this is deemed appropriate for 'Life Protection'. It is the distinction between the background levels and the levels required for life protection that cause the problems we so often see, coupled with incompetent or inappropriate usage of 'off-the-shelf' devices.

6.8 Isolated Supplies

The second use of the term 'isolation' refers to a type of supply that has had any reference to ground removed by use of an 'isolating' transformer. Normally, when the incoming supply is reduced from the high voltage lines from the national grid, the transformer is configured in such a way as to fix the live conductors at the nominal above earth. By using an Isolated Supply, we eliminate a reference to earth and the potential difference is between the two cables from the transformer. In the event of a fault, one side of the supply becomes referenced to whatever is causing the fault. Only in the event of two simultaneous faults does it become dangerous. As long as the system is regularly checked, an isolated supply can minimise the effects of a simple fault on the human body to a slight, momentary tingling.

Often, isolating transformers have a new reference to earth attached. While this eliminates the benefit of the dual fault situation, the supply is still isolated because there is electrical separation from the main supply. Examples of this are:

The yellow 110V transformers seen on most of the building sites in the UK that provide additional protection to the user by reducing the maximum voltage to 55V, by using a centre tapped earth.

Sound companies use transformers to remove mains-born noise from supplies to sensitive audio equipment. Often these transformers have one live connected to earth to re-reference the supply.

Two transformers: one centre tapped; other isolated with ground reference.

7

PROTECTIVE DEVICES
(AND THEIR SHORTCOMINGS)

7.1 Fuses

Fuses are no more and no less than a deliberate 'weak link' in the electrical chain. Any piece of wire has resistance, and therefore will heat up whenever an electrical current flows through it. In a normal cable, the size of the conductor is chosen so that the heat created does not exceed certain limits, determined by the construction of the insulation. In a fuse, the temperatures are allowed to get much higher, and when the

Sample fuses.

fault current has been exceeded, the wire melts, and the link is broken. There are various types of fuses, some with coils, some just straight wires. This is all part of the design of the fuse.

You may have heard of anti-surge, or slow-blow fuses. Some fuses are designed to be able to sustain an over-current condition for a short period of time, to avoid nuisance tripping in electric hoists or transformers; others are designed to blow with a relatively small amount of over current, and are designed to be used with equipment that may have a fault condition which may only be a partial short circuit. Fuses will always blow when they reach the correct part of their operating curve (current vs. time). They can be a nuisance to replace, and may require the system to be powered down, but as a last resort, they are unbeatable. They are the only protective devices that are designed to fail, so to speak.

In higher current applications, you may hear of fuses called HRC, which stands for High Rupture Capacity. These are often sand filled because vaporised air conducts. This same theory is used inside some nuclear reactors, as the sand melts and turns into glass. In the fuse it simply replaces the conductor with an insulator. In the reactor it traps radioactive material and seals it.

7.2 Circuit Breakers

Circuit breakers are protective devices that sense over-current, and when they do, they operate a switch to turn off the circuit. They may sense the over current thermally or magnetically, but to the end user, this should not be an issue. What is an issue is that just like fuses, there are different types for different applications, but they are not fail safe. Because they operate a switch, they can fail under excessive fault currents.

If you read the manufacturer's information closely, you will see a maximum break current. This is the ability of the device to disconnect any fault current up to that level. It may be 6kA, or 10kA for the smaller MCB devices, which is a fault current easily created by a dead short.

When this massive overload occurs, the 'switch' starts to operate, but as the contact area between the two halves of the switch is reduced, massive heating (and usually arcing) takes place which can melt the poles. This in turn can 'weld' the two contacts together, which prevents the protective device from operating. Because of this it is very important to look at your distribution

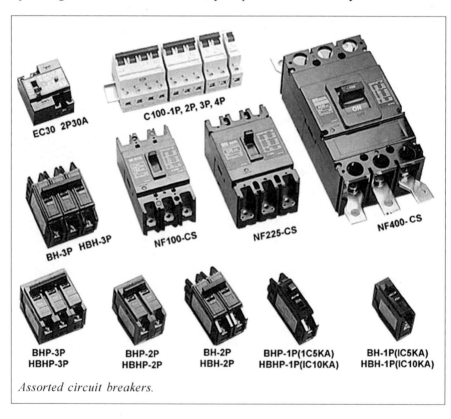

Assorted circuit breakers.

equipment as a system, and not a collection of individual bits of equipment.

Many manufacturers of circuit breakers recommend a back-up fuse, which is deliberately overrated to allow the circuit breaker to operate under non-catastrophic failures, but under a dead short, it will blow quickly enough to protect the breaker. If you look carefully at you own house, you will notice that the electricity board has its own set of fuses, separate from your distribution board. Ever wondered why?

You may also find that some circuit breakers have a maximum and minimum operating voltage. Outside these boundaries, the device may fail to operate properly. This is also worth checking. Low current circuit breakers in the UK are often referred to as MCBs - Miniature Circuit Breakers – although this term is really reserved for the type that is designed to fit into a standard sized distribution board with DIN rail mounts.

7.3 Shunt Trips

Some circuit breakers have an additional facility which allows an add-on device or sensor to trigger the disconnection of the load. These are known as shunt trips. They are most commonly used in high current applications (more than 63 Amps), and may be used in conjunction with devices that sense frequency, under/over voltage and earth faults. In large machinery they are often used to provide a zero volt release, so that in the event of a power failure the equipment cannot suddenly start up again without warning.

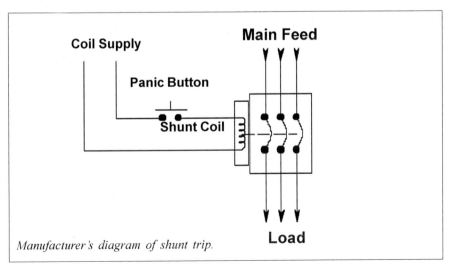

Manufacturer's diagram of shunt trip.

7.4 Earth Leakage Circuit Breakers (ELCB)

An ELCB is not the same as an RCD. The ELCB was a design which sensed current flowing down the earth conductor and when that current was over a prescribed limit, it would trip. ELCBs are not used in this country any more, and haven't been for some time, but it is important that the distinction is made between it and an RCD. The problem with the ELCB was that it had no way of knowing where the current that was flowing down the earth wire came from, nor was there any guarantee that a fault in your equipment wasn't flowing down someone else's earth wire.

7.5 Residual Current Devices (RCD)

A Residual Current Device (originally also known as an RCCB, Residual Current Circuit Breaker) measures the differences between the current flowing up to the load, and the return path. This is done, quite simply, by passing all the conductors (excluding the earth) through a coil. Because of cancellations, the coil will only pick up an imbalance, which means that the remaining current is flowing to earth, somewhere in the system. In order for an RCD to offer life protection, it must trip at below 30mA, and within 40ms. This is a tough job and early designs were prone to failure under the stresses of daily life on the road. Cheaper devices will still fail, and therefore for these devices to be used successfully, they must be regularly tested, and not only by just pushing the test button on the front of the device. That only confirms that the device still works, but not at what level of fault. (Please see advanced issues later.)

If you use a third party RCD (sub-hired, rented or in a venue), you should always ask to see a current test certificate. If the equipment has not be properly installed and maintained, all you have is a false sense of security. You have no way of knowing if it will work properly until it is too late.

7.6 RCBO

An RCBO (Residual Current Breaker / Overload) is a combination of an MCB and a RCD. They are a useful space saving device, but as always, the combination will always be a compromise. In some applications they will be fine, in others you may just not find the type you want.

7.7 ELV/PELV/SELV

Extra Low Voltage is a way of reducing the risk to a person by reducing the voltage (i.e. below 50V AC). This means that there is less risk of arcing, less stress on insulation, and for any given resistance, less current capable of flowing. **Protective Extra Low Voltage** uses an isolation transformer to reduce the live voltage, but still retains an earth reference.

Separated Extra Low Voltage uses an isolation transformer where we deliberately end up with two floating lives, rather than one live and one neutral. The reason for this is that a single fault will reference that line to the fault, and it will require a second, simultaneous fault on the other live, before an electric shock can be created.

8 CABLES AND CONNECTORS

8.1 Extension Cables

When we use a single piece of equipment, and it is connected by a flexible piece of cable, invariably we introduce the concept of an extension cable. The risk of using an extension cable over a fixed installation is that the electrical system designer can no longer rely on a fixed distance to the equipment, and therefore all the calculations for earth loop impedances may no longer be valid.

The use of the term 'extension' cable conjures up other risks as well, trip hazards, the ability to accidentally cut through it with a power tool, etc.

It is for this reason that so many people insist that RCD protection is used

A thousand-word picture!

when extension cables are present. When used with a single piece of equipment, or even a fairly restricted set of logically grouped equipment (e.g. Front Of House), using an RCD can be part of an effective electrical design.

One of the problems facing a large temporary installation is that the usual 30mA rating is no longer suitable for the higher background levels of earth leakage. Instead of looking at our temporary distribution system as a collection of extension cables, it should be considered as a temporary replacement for a permanent installation, and should be subject to the same good design practices.

Most of the time we run cables in carefully chosen routes, protected by the stage set, barriers, cable troughs, grouped and often triped together for neatness as well as ease of rigging and de-rigging. The major difference from a traditional installation is that our cables are not fixed to a wall, buried under the floor or run in conduit. In most cases this provides little additional protection for a properly organised and maintained temporary mains distribution system.

Temporary	Fixed
Flexible cable	Armoured Cable
Plug & Socket	Hard-wired
Double-insulated wiring	Single-insulated + trunking
Ramps and cable picks	Fixed to walls
Multicore	Single core
BS7909	BS7671

Comparison of temporary and fixed wiring methodology.

8.2 Multicores

It is important to distinguish between the two main types of multicore cables we use, namely single circuit and multi-circuit. A single circuit cable may be single phase or three phase, anywhere between two core for a separated extra low voltage circuit, up to seven cores - three phase, neutral and earth circuit with an interlock system.

A multi-circuit multicore contains a number of separate circuits, which are electrically separated by protective devices. Usually they are single phase three core circuits, but it may well be that they are connected to multiple phases, and therefore the insulation must be rated the same as, if not higher than, a three phase cable.

Because of the semi-standardisation of the industry, different companies use the same connectors for different purposes. Lighting companies use 19 pin Socapex type connectors to feed six lamp circuits, but some sound companies use the same system to feed speaker clusters. If in doubt, don't touch and go and ask someone who knows.

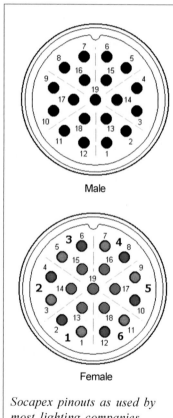

Male

Female

Socapex pinouts as used by most lighting companies.

8.3 PVC versus Rubber

The two main types of insulation materials used are PVC (Polyvinyl Chloride) and Rubber. PVC is cheaper, less flexible, and has a narrower temperature band. It doesn't coil well and is very stiff, particularly in cold weather. Rubber, on the other hand is far nicer to handle. Toughened Rubber Sheath, or TRS as it is often known, is far more durable and flexible than PVC, is usually rated at a maximum of 85°C (as opposed to 70°C for PVC), which is why you can generally run higher currents down a TRS cable than a same sized PVC one.

However, most custom built cables, including Socapex type multicores, are PVC because they are much easier to manufacture.

Either way, any time you try and coil a cable you usually end up in a mess at some point. This is usually due to the way the cable is made, and then put on a drum. Because of this all cables have a natural tendency to want to coil a certain way. People will tell you any number of ways to get round it, but there is only one way that reliably works, which is to always start from the same end, and always uncoil the reverse of the way you coiled it. If you try to fight the natural twist in the cable you will take a lot longer to get to the pub at the end of the gig.

8.4 Copper versus Aluminium

There are two main types of material used in conductors for cables: copper and aluminium. Copper is a far better conductor than aluminium, but it is heavier, so in some cases, the extra girth of the aluminium cable is worth the lower weight. Once you get up to single core 400A cable, you may see the benefits of a lighter cable. Personally, I prefer the benefits of using stage crew…

8.5 Domestic Connectors

There are a number of domestic connectors in use within our industry, and we must be aware that these connectors are not necessarily fit for purpose.

The prime example is the 13A plug. It was developed as a way of ensuring adequate protection when connected to a 30A ring main, which is a very clever way of reducing your cabling costs in a house by running a loop, providing two current carrying paths back from the supply from any socket. The 13A plug allows you to reduce the size of the cable coming from the socket (which is rated at 13A), via the plug with a fuse. You can reduce the size of the cable by de-rating the fuse. However, this fuse may restrict your ability to properly discriminate between faults, and make fault-finding and fixing a much harder task.

Assorted domestic plugs.

A 6 and 10 Amp IEC socket and plug combination.

The round pin plug system (5A and 15A) pre-dates the 13A system. Its usage became common within the lighting industry due to its lack of a fuse, which was the main reason it became obsolete as a domestic connector.

The IEC, or Euro plug is a 6 Amp connector commonly found on a lot of control equipment and computers. It is a connector that is multi-voltage, so it can be used in many applications where the power supply can accept a wide range of supplies. The problem in using this connector is that since its inception, a pin-compatible 'hot' 10 Amp version has been released. Unless you are very careful, you may find that you end up mixing the two versions, and your protective device may be set at 10 Amps rather than the lower value of 6 Amps required by some of the connectors. Higher ratings of IEC connectors are also available.

8.6 Industrial Connectors

There is a range of industrial connectors, incorrectly referred to as 'Cee-Form', which are very useful to us. They are colour-coded and cannot be cross-plugged. They conform to a European standard (EN60309 (also referred to as IEC 603 and superseded BS 4343)). The ground rules for using them are simple.

Colour Code: The colours shown in the table opposite refer to the voltage range allowed in the circuit. They are non-negotiable as far as any safety rules are concerned, and the colour has *no* relevance to the number of live conductors.

Colour	Circuit Voltage
Purple	20 to 25V
White	40 to 50V
Yellow	100 to 130V
Blue	200 to 250V
Red	380 to 480V
Black	500 to 690V
Green	Over 60 to 500Hz

Connector Pins: The pins are pre-assigned, just like a 13 amp plug. You must not use them for anything else. The earth pin is longer than the rest so that it connects first and disconnects last. Live pins are referred to as poles, and not all have a neutral. For example, a five pin, three-phase connector will be marked as '3P+N+E'. A three pin connector is marked as '2P+E', so that it can be used with isolated supplies as well as the more usual Live, Neutral and Earth three-wire circuit we all know and love. When you get inside one to wire it up you may find that one of the poles is marked up as neutral to avoid confusion. It should be noted that some connectors have additional pins for use with an interlock system.

Current Ratings: There are four current ratings within the range: 16, 32, 63 and 125 Amps. Within each range, there can be connectors of any voltage range, and number of poles. Only the 16 Amp series are rated for disconnection under load (but please don't unless you have to.). The 63 and 125 Amp versions will weld themselves together quicker than you can pull them apart, and there are also reports that the 125 Amp connector overheats at full capacity, so some companies in our industry (especially film and TV) have fitted 100 Amp protective devices to all their 125 Amp distribution system. I hasten

A selection of industrial connectors.

to add that the manufacturers are very keen to see any examples of this and tend to blame any problems on cheap imports and dirty contacts (higher resistance, more heat).

8.7 Single Pole Connectors

A large chunk of this industry relies heavily on single pole connectors. There are a number of systems available, but the most common at the moment are the 'CamLok', the 'BAC' and the 'PowerLock'. The CamLok is an American connector, originally developed for welding equipment, and the BAC was developed by the British Aerospace Corporation to connect ground power to aircraft. The BAC is primarily used by the TV and Film Industry, whereas the CamLok was adopted by the 'rock and roll' concert touring companies. The PowerLock connector was designed specifically for the entertainment industry and it aims to address the requirements of this sector.

Many people have differing opinions about the different connectors and their legalities. Here is the best slant I can give you on the issue:

BAC: The BAC connector has a BS number (BS 5550 - Part 7.5), which is now no longer considered current. The connector is not commonly available any more, so is falling from usage. It has the advantage of having finger protection on the socket, but has no colour coding in any way.

CamLok: The CamLok conforms to no British or European standards, and has only recently received a UL listing. It is colour coded, but has no finger protection in the socket, and the strain relief system can be difficult to use. Any CamLok can be interconnected regardless of designation and all connectors are the same.

PowerLock: Litton-Veam has developed a connector that conformed to the same construction standards as the IEC 309 industrial connectors, but as there is no dimension standard for a single-pole connector yet, they cannot claim full conformity. PowerLocks are designed to prevent incorrect connection as they have keyways that designate the connector as either an earth neutral or phase.

CamLok single-pole connectors.

So the BAC is actually the only current connector with full British Standard recognition but the standard is obsolescent. There is no law that 'outlaws' a connector in an industrial situation, only that it must be safe and fit for purpose. Because there is no finger protection, some people assume it must be unsafe; but it is only unsafe if it is powered up at the time, and that comes down to safe working practices.

PowerLock connectors.

I have no doubt that the PowerLock and its clones will eventually take over from both the CamLok and the BAC, but at the moment the bottom line is that a single pole connector system is as unsafe as the person responsible for it. There have been moves both here and in the States to introduce a sequential coupling system so that you can only connect in the correct sequence, but as none of these connectors can be disconnected under load, to make it idiot-proof you would also have to add some sort of interlock. However, each successive device adds complexity, increasing the risk of failure, thus it becomes more dangerous than it was.

If you use a CamLok set safely, they will be safe. If you never connect or disconnect live, always follow the correct connection and disconnection sequence, follow the colour code, maintain the connectors, and prevent tampering your system will be as safe as necessary. A 400Amp single-pole system can never be compared with a multi-pole connector. The potential for damage to both persons and equipment is massive, and if a single pole connector needs to be idiot-proof, don't employ idiots!

8.8 Current Ratings and Splitter Cables
Whenever you change current ratings (or connector sizes) you must consider the effects this has on the protective devices. For example, if you take a 63 Amp connector and wire it to two 32A sockets, unless your protective device is rated at 32 Amps, you may have a situation where up to 63 Amps could be drawn through one of the connectors without a fuse or circuit breaker doing

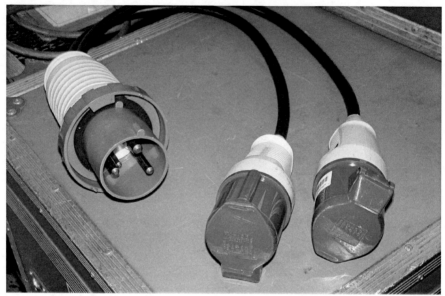

How not to do it: a bad splitter cable.

anything about it, because the circuit is correctly rated at 63 Amps.

Every time you reduce the current carrying capacity of a circuit, you must reduce the rating of the protective device. In our example above, there are two ways of solving this problem. The first would be that the cable splitter is actually a box that contains two additional protective devices, one for each socket. The second solution is for the cable splitter to have two 63 Amp sockets, and for the subsequent distribution box to contain the relevant fuses or circuit breakers.

Either way, an adapter cable that reduces the size of a connector is potentially dangerous. Only in certain situations will it be safe to use, and can you ever be sure that it will only be used in this situation.

When working out the maximum current requirements of a system, you need to be sure that each circuit can carry the demand. That is quite easy. When you come to calculate the total load, the system loads may not necessarily all be on at once, so you may be able use a smaller supply than the maximum. However, under these conditions, it is very important that accidental or improper usage of the system does not overload the system. Situations where the operator is not electrically competent can be very scary, and some newer dimmer control systems can limit the overall current to a pre-set system maximum.

9 THREE PHASE

9.1 What is Three Phase (3Ø)?

Three-phase power is a transmission system based on the theory that three sine waves, 120 degrees out of phase, will cancel out. This means that a three-phase load that produces a sine current waveform requires no neutral cable as it produces no neutral current.

Three-phase electricity is produced by a generator where rotor armature windings are set at 120° to each other, so that when the rotor turns, three separate currents are produced, separated by the same phase shift.

In some systems, it means that three times the amount of power can be transmitted with only one more cable, which has a major cost implication.

However, three-phase systems can also be used to derive three single-phase supplies as it is impractical to expect a small system (by 'small' I mean under 63A single-phase) to be able to balance the phases properly. We are not just talking about the amount of current, but the 'type' of current. The current

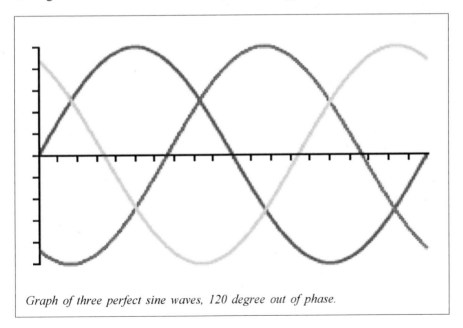

Graph of three perfect sine waves, 120 degree out of phase.

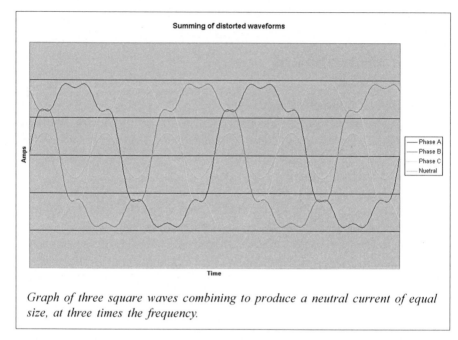

Summing of distorted waveforms

Amps

Time

Phase A
Phase B
Phase C
Nuetral

Graph of three square waves combining to produce a neutral current of equal size, at three times the frequency.

waveforms must also be the correct shape for cancellation to occur, and this will only occur if the waveform is a sine wave.

When the load is purely resistive, or the amounts of capacitance and inductance are equal, in other words, a 'passive' load, the current waveform, whether leading or lagging, will remain a sine wave. However, as soon as some sort of dynamic or active load is used, invariably the neutral current will start to rise.

Most people work under the impression that a neutral current can never be more than a phase current, but in these days of switch mode power supplies, it is not uncommon to see neutral currents in excess of 1.5 times the highest phase current.

9.2 Star or Y

Star (also referred to as Y) is where the load is connected between a phase and the neutral. A three-phase load uses four wires (+ earth) connected together in a Y, where the neutral is the centre, and the loads are the legs. Star is very easily converted to single-phase distribution as long as care is taken with balancing the load and attention is paid to the neutral current.

9.3 Delta or Δ

Delta (or Δ) is where the load is connected between two phases. A three phase load only needs three wires (+ protective earth) but the return currents of each phase flow back down the other two phase wires. Load balancing can become crucial as, instead of having a strange neutral current, it is all returned down the same cables, and phase currents have a habit of never matching the maths in a complex distribution system.

A delta supply cannot easily be used for single phase supplies. It usually requires a three-phase transformer to convert from delta to star instead. However, in places where the phase-to-phase voltage is similar to the phase to neutral voltages we require (eg USA: 208V, or some parts of Spain, Belgium and

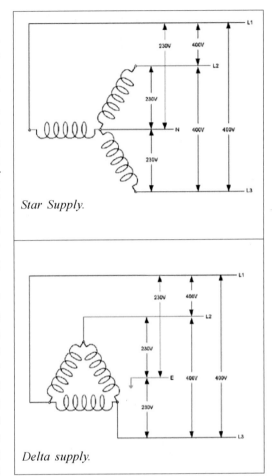

Star Supply.

Delta supply.

Norway: 220V), you can run a load between two phase wires, as long as the load does not use the neutral as some sort of earth reference, and the equipment uses double-pole switches and breakers. This is definitely not recommended practice unless the equipment has been designed with this usage in mind, as your equipment will have a neutral to ground potential of 120V!

9.4 TN-C, TN-S, TN-C-S, TT, IT

These initials all refer to the way a three-phase system is connected together, and they are all legitimate ways of distributing a supply in the right place.

TN-C: This method uses a combined protective conductor and neutral, so in effect there are only four wires.

TN-S: This method is a five-wire system, running a separate earth and neutral, where the two are bonded together at the substation, and all five cables are then run to the distribution panels.

TN-C-S: This is a combination of the two methods described above, where it only uses four wires behind the scenes, but splits out the earth as a separate wire as it enters a distribution unit, so it appears as a five wire system in the box.

TT: TT is a four-wire system where the neutral is bonded to earth at the supply end, but is not used as the protective conductor. A local earth spike is used at the end of the circuit.

IT: IT only uses three wires, as it uses no neutral and a local earth. The supply earth reference, if required, is picked up via an impedance, not directly connected.

10 TEST EQUIPMENT

10.1 True RMS

RMS (Root Mean Square) is a method that has been developed to improve the accuracy of non-sine wave signals. A cheap multimeter uses an averaging technique using a simple rectifier, either half wave or full wave. A measurement at this point, averaged over time, will show a value of 0.637 of peak value of the waveform (for full wave rectification, ignoring any losses).

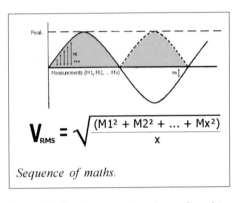

$$V_{RMS} = \sqrt{\frac{(M1^2 + M2^2 + \ldots + Mx^2)}{x}}$$

Sequence of maths.

However, in a purely mathematical world, the 'average' value of a sine wave is zero, and therefore RMS is a way of getting a meaningful value that will hold up whatever waveform is being measured.

RMS is the root of the average of the sum of the square of successive snapshot measurements of a waveform. By taking a snapshot measurement and squaring it, we eliminate the effects of the negative part of the cycle. By taking an average over time, we remove the effects of the periodic rise and fall of the waveform, and by taking the root of the result, we get back to a meaningful value. In a sine wave, the RMS value is 0.707 of the peak.

So when you buy a cheap meter, it 'sees' a value of 0.637, and multiplies it by 1.111 to get a simulated RMS value. This may be fine for voltage waveforms, where the total distortion may only be a couple of percent, and are usually due to the rest of the national grid doing weird things, but it completely negates any current measurements on anything other than a purely resistive load.

The moral of the story is that if you are using a meter to measure current, buy a true RMS multimeter; anything less is only going to confuse you, give you false readings, and make everyone else question your sanity.

10.2 High Impedance Devices

Following in the footsteps of Heisenberg's Principle of Uncertainty,

Schrödinger's Cat and the Butterfly Effect, how can you be sure that when you measure a circuit, you aren't distorting the measurement by altering the circuit with your meter?

Well, you are. The trick is to reduce the effect to a level where the error becomes part of a general lack of accuracy. Every device will have an input impedance, and if you are measuring voltage, either with a meter or an oscilloscope, the higher the impedance the better. If the input impedance of the device is less than 1% of the circuit you are measuring, you will have very little effect on the measurement, given the general accuracy of your test equipment.

Conversely, if you are measuring in-circuit current (as opposed to a clamp meter, see later), the lower the impedance the better.

However, you must also understand what is going on in the circuit you are measuring before you can rely on the meter. If you have a high impedance circuit, you may find that you start to measure the effects of static or induction from a nearby circuit. You may also be measuring across a device that controls a waveform. An example of this is a load light on a dimmer. This will normally only light up when the dimmer channel is 'off', but the circuit is complete. Because the neon bypasses the dimmer, it allows mains voltage to flow to the lamp and back down the neutral. Because of the high impedance of the neon, it reduces the current in the circuit, and the low resistance of the lamp is so low it has little effect on the circuit until the dimmer channel comes on. At this point the load light goes out.

In a fault condition, you may end up measuring mains voltage that actually comes via the neon, not via the dimmer channel.

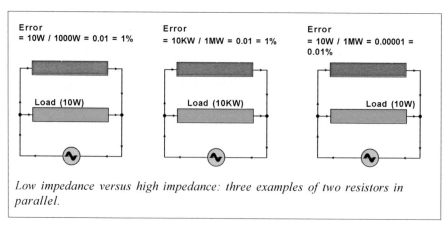

Low impedance versus high impedance: three examples of two resistors in parallel.

10.3 The Light Bulb

When you get a reading you are unsure about, one trick is to apply a load to the same point you measured. A good visual indication is a lamp. The load needs to be rated for the worst case, but by changing the way the circuit is wired, you will know whether you are chasing a phantom. If the lamp comes on, you can measure the voltage across it and you now know you aren't going mad.

10.4 Voltmeters

When you use a voltmeter, you need to check that the input impedance is appropriate to the work you are doing.

You also need to check that the voltage rating, type of probes, and fusing are all appropriate to the task you will be doing. If you are metering mains, will it go high enough for phase-to-phase measurements? What sort of input protection does it have, and are the probes fused and properly insulated?

Finally: do you need a true RMS meter?

10.5 Clamp Meters

A clamp meter is a non-invasive way of measuring power. It uses magnetic waves produced by the electrical current to generate a signal in the clamp, which can then be measured and with some maths, which can approximate the value of the current in the conductor.

They are generally less accurate at lower currents (less than 20A), and because the influence of external interference is greater, they are optimised for specific frequencies (usually 50/60Hz), and have to go around a single conductor (unless you want the sum of two or more conductors), which is why we all love single core cable in large systems.

It really makes no sense to get anything other than a true RMS meter. The error for an

Some clamp meters.

averaging system could be as much as 100% in a system with a lot of dimmers at half power. I have seen 600 Amps measured on a system that only had 400 Amp fuses. In those situations the meter isn't even any good as a stage weight!

10.6 Others: Insulation, Earth Loop, P.A.T.

Other test equipment you may come across will include:

Insulation Tester: This equipment checks the insulation of a conductor by charging it with a voltage (usually 300 or 500V) and measuring the resistance, which should be in the megohm range. In the case of an appliance they usually common together the phase and the neutral conductors to protect the equipment from the test voltage.

Continuity Tester: This is usually either a very cheap device used to 'bleep out' circuits, or it is a high quality resistance meter capable of measuring down to 0.01 Ohms. Don't get confused between the two.

Earth Loop Impedance Tester: This equipment will measure the impedance from the supply, down to ground, and give you a maximum fault current, which allows you to check if your protective device will react quickly enough.

Portable Appliance Tester: This equipment is a combination of a number of devices, packaged together into what approximates to an idiot-proof system. It will test insulation, earth bond, load and leakage currents, and often has a flash test facility, which you should never have to use.

RCD tester: The test button on an RCD rarely does more than test that the relay still works. An RCD tester applies specific current and times how long it takes to react. If you use RCDs for life protection, at a minimum you should have access to this piece of equipment.

Oscilloscope: An Oscilloscope is of limited use for electrical testing until you are very deep into a problem. It is not a purchase that the average person needs to make, unless they really want to spend enough money on one that does voltage and current readings as well.

Component tester: These devices will measure the non-resistive loads such as capacitors and coils. They can be very useful when measuring a transformer winding, which, when using a DC continuity tester will show a very low reading and wouldn't show if half the windings were shorted out.

Power Analyser: These devices can be very useful as they will show power factors, real power, phase voltages, etc. They are usually best when permanently mounted into a main distribution unit, but beware those that simulate three-phase readings from a single current clamp.

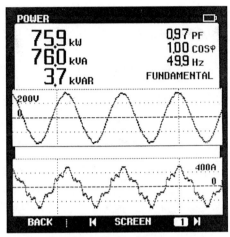

Screen shot from Fluke 47 power analyser.

Volt-stick: They come under many names, but they often use the same principle as the clamp meter to show the presence of current. They can be misleading, as they don't always work unless there is a current flowing, so check before you buy.

Neon screwdriver: A very useful device made to use your body's natural electrical potential to sink a small amount of current, by connecting you to the mains via a neon lamp. It will show the presence of an electrical supply, but don't bet your life on the result.

Frequency Meter: In most cases you will not need to know what the mains frequency is, but if you are running a generator, you might want to check what happen when the load has a sudden change - not a lot of use if the display updates slowly, so be careful with your choice.

10.7 How to Interpret the Results

Whenever you get a result on a piece of measuring equipment, you need to understand the data. In the simplest terms, you need to know if the equipment works. If you are trying to measure a circuit that is supposed to be dead, do you know if your meter is working properly?

Even if you do get a result, is it the one you were expecting? If not, where is the problem? Is there a problem at all?

When you connect up a distribution system to a three-phase supply, you check the inter-connections between all five wires (assuming a Y supply). From the data you receive you should be able to interpret if you indeed have three phases, if you have a floating earth, and whether the neutral looks good.

First you measure phase to neutral, once for each of the three phases. One would expect these results to be very slightly different, which could be due to a phase imbalance elsewhere in the building. You then measure from phase to

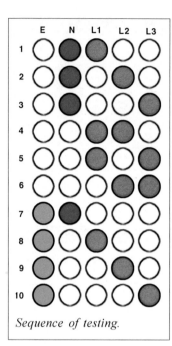

	E	N	L1	L2	L3
1	○	●	●	○	○
2	○	●	○	●	○
3	○	●	○	○	●
4	○	○	●	●	○
5	○	○	●	○	●
6	○	○	○	●	●
7	●	●	○	○	○
8	●	○	●	○	○
9	●	○	○	●	○
10	●	○	○	○	●

Sequence of testing.

phase (three measurements) and should get another three, almost identical, results, all of which may vary slightly due to loads elsewhere.

The next measurement is neutral to ground, which should make sense as to the small differences you have seen on the previous six measurements. Usually, the neutral has a small amount of voltage caused by the resistance of the cable between the substation and wherever your cable is connected to the busbars.

The final measurements are between ground and the three phases. Unless there is either a high level of earth leakage, or the earth connection is of poor quality, these three measurements should be almost identical. By measuring to earth, the only differences you should see will be due to manufacturing differences in the substation transformers, or an indication of an overloaded phase (where the transformer system is no longer regulating the voltage properly), or the result of earth current flowing in the system, which might be the indication of faulty equipment elsewhere, or the result of a bad earthing system.

All the voltages measured here relate to each other. If you look at all the measurements in context, they will be able to tell you a lot about the quality of the installation. If you look at just one measurement, in isolation from the rest, you cannot tell anything about what else is going on. A keen sense of how these ten measurements relate to each other will tell you a lot in a very short period of time.

We must also be aware that our usage of an electrical supply is dynamic. Things may change as loads increase, and the measurements we took at the beginning of the day have become meaningless. It is very useful to have the facility to measure the supply voltages, but it is most useful to be able to perform those measurements with the same equipment, so that the results not only bear relevance among themselves, but also the previous set of results. By connecting your load, you will start to see the effects of ill health in your own system; excessive earth leakage, unbalanced loads, weird neutral currents, etc.

In the world of electrical supplies, "What You See Is What You Get" is not applicable. It's usually in what you don't see that the problem lies. Look for corroborating data, especially from a different angle. Look for the discrepancies and, if in doubt, check, double check, and then check again, throughout the day. Don't expect a house electrician to notice a problem. Often you actually have to show them the source of the problem, not just the symptoms, before they will be able to look into it. And by then, it may be too late to get a generator.

11 LOADS
(AND THEIR PROBLEMS)

If all our loads were simple light bulbs, controlled by on/off switches, and performers projected to the back of the hall without electronic assistance, our lives would be a lot simpler. Boring, but simpler.

11.1 Dimmers

The way basic dimmers work (and yes, it does get a lot more complicated than this) is to control the output by chopping the waveform. The supply is fed into an electronic switch (usually a thyristor or triac), which turns off automatically when the incoming voltage crosses zero (which it will do 100 times a second in the UK), and is turned on at a point in time related to the control requirements. This means

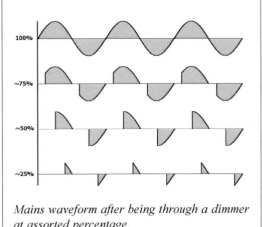

Mains waveform after being through a dimmer at assorted percentage.

that a lamp at 50% is turned on half-way through the cycle. It will always receive close to 100% of the live voltage if the control signal is switched on before the cycle peaks.

What this means from a load point of view is that we are only loading the cycle for part of the time, rather than partly loading it. The current waveform becomes very distorted, and anything other than a true RMS meter is useless.

A large rig can have very strange effect on the supply if the whole system is brought up at 50%. This is because all sorts of things are happening that can confuse regulating circuits. The excessive neutral currents may overload the cable (remember most neutral cabling isn't protected), and the amount of harmonic noise produced can cause breakers and RCDs to trip when nothing is actually at fault.

11.2 Switch Mode Power Supplies

Switched mode power supplies have made their way into all sorts of equipment these days. They are lightweight, small, and can usually accept a wide range of input voltages and frequencies. They also present a horrible load to the supply. Basically what they do is rectify the mains, and charge a set of capacitors up to live voltage. The supply then uses that stored voltage to create a high frequency (often around 20kHz), runs it through a small transformer (small because of the high frequency), to get a voltage it can deal with.

The PSU only needs to take current from the supply to make up the difference between the live voltage and the capacitors, so the current tends only to flow just before the waveform reaches its peak. This produces a very nasty current waveform that is often smoothed out by filtering. However, a lot of arc lamps, and some of the newer power amplifiers are now using these types of PSUs, and while this has the benefit of smoothing out some of the peaks and demands over a long period, on a cycle by cycle basis, your neutral current has a habit of not cancelling out. Nasty!

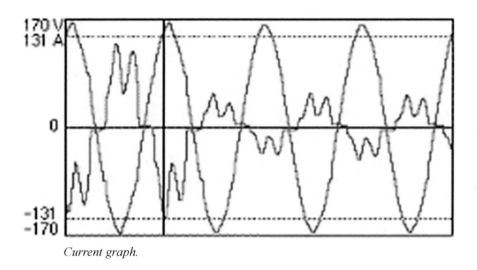

Current graph.

11.3 Transformers

A transformer load is as close to a purely inductive load as you will ever find. If you use a transformer after a dimmer, this inductance can have a weird effect on the dimmer control circuit, and end up not working at all as you expected.

On the other hand, a transformer used properly can have lots of useful applications. From a safety point of view, using an isolating transformer can make a lot of the on-stage equipment much safer. It can help to filter out the effects of harmonics generated elsewhere in the distribution system, and therefore cut out some of the hum produced by the dimmers that finds its way to a guitar pickup.

A transformer will always take a surge of current when it is first turned on, even with no load. This surge is produced by the coils 'charging' themselves up with a magnetic field. For this reason there are different types of breakers and fuses designed to cope with a high but short surge of current. As good practice, you should never power up a large transformer (i.e. greater than 500Va) with a load connected. The greater the load, the greater the surge, as it has to supply not only the load, but the magnetic field as well. This also slows down the speed at which the transformer produces its output voltage, so the load is presented with a lower than expected live voltage, which can produce problems in the load as well, blowing internal fuses, or taking out power supplies that auto switch voltage ranges.

When you turn off the supply to a transformer, the magnetic field collapses, and a surge is produced which will dissipate anywhere it can. You may have noticed diodes across the coils of DC relays. These are there to dissipate that surge, which is known as 'back EMF'. If your load is still connected at this point, the back EMF will find its way to it.

11.4 Neon and Fluorescent
Neon and fluorescent lighting often ends up being used within lighting systems for special effects or set pieces.Both, however, can present a problem when it comes to control. Neons require a high voltage power supply and there is a choice of a transformer that can provide basic on/off functions or a high frequency electronic unit that is dimmable via DMX. Fluorescents also require a power supply, known as a ballast, to drive each specific lamp wattage, i.e. a 70W tube needs a 70W ballast. Because fluorescents come from the domestic market, it is often possible to use off-the-shelf control gear but it doesn't necessarily fit with entertainment-based equipment, so it is best to check with manufacturers. With both of these types of lamp it is also important to find out what type of control is required: is it a sophisticated chase or a straightforward on /off? Once this is established, it is more likely that the correct solution can be found for the required effect.

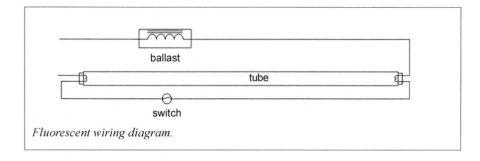

Fluorescent wiring diagram.

11.5 Amplifiers

Conventional amplifiers usually use a large transformer/rectifier/capacitor based power supply. They try to rely on the storage of the capacitors to supply any peaks required by the amplifier itself. Cunning designers have paralleled up different types and sizes of capacitors to cope with surges at different frequencies, using the variation in internal resistance to cope with high frequency bursts and low frequency throbs.

Somehow, this all ends up pulling power from the supply. The transformer always requires a background current to keep the magnetic fields from collapsing (with the subsequent back-EMF and start-up surges). Because the supply is trying to keep a capacitor bank full, the current is only pulled from the supply during, and just before, the peaks. If you see major amounts of current being pulled after the peak, it may mean that your amplifier cannot charge itself up enough to sustain the next half cycle's worth of 'umph'. This could be due to the fact that the amplifier is trying too hard and is starting to clip, or that the PSU transformer is too small, or that the amp is overloaded by a speaker load that is too low in resistance (e.g. 2Ohm rather than 4Ohm).

12 POWER SOURCES
(AND THEIR PROBLEMS)

We see a socket on the wall, we assume the supply is something we can use, and off we go. Just where does it all come from, and what problems will this cause?

12.1 National Grid

Most countries use the concept of a national grid, where all the power stations are connected to a large scale backbone supplying power to anywhere in the country. As power demands change, most stations can either be brought into line, or put on standby.

The heaviest demand for power is usually during the day, when all the factories are working, so in order to keep power stations at maximum efficiency, night-time supplies are often cheaper.

There are even 'storage' facilities which use off peak power to pump water into a lake, and then reverses the flow using gravity to power generators within seconds of the demand being required.

Even though there is this massive infrastructure, local demands can easily upset the voltage levels that you may see, and frequently the voltage levels will change just before show time! However, because all the generators connected to the national grid need to be synchronised, the frequency should remain steady.

12.2 Generators

Generators come in many sizes and can be optimised for the type of load they face. Generators are rated in volt-amperes, and have a power factor of about 0.8.

You have to pick the rating of a generator quite carefully. Too small and it may stall on full load, too large and it may not have enough load to tick over properly. Often two generators are tied together, one small, one large, so that the operator can power up one and shut down the other without the load being affected.

Most generators are diesel or gas powered. Either way, having a generator

Two different types of generator.

run out of fuel, or suffer from fuel starvation can have a very damaging effect on your load. As the generator slows down, the frequency drops, and any transformers in your load (especially toroidal) will pull more current, causing fuses to blow, and pulling the voltage down so that auto-ranging power supplies change down to their lower range. As the transformer fuses blow, the voltage may spike, blowing up the auto-ranging supplies.

Just like car engines, generators have flywheels. A large flywheel will help to balance out a dynamic load and maintain a consistent frequency, but will be slower to recover from a massive current surge. A small flywheel will be more affected by a sudden surge, and the frequency will drop, but will also be able to get back up to speed more quickly.

Most generators have no ground reference. They provide a completely isolated supply from the rest of the world. First of all you will need to get a good earth from somewhere, and secondly you will need to decide whether the generator neutral should be referenced to ground. If you have a purely three-phase load, this is less important, but with single-phase loads, a floating neutral can be pulled up to the level of a phase, resulting in all the equipment on the other two phases receiving 400 Volts.

12.3 UPSs

An Uninterruptible Power Supply is a device that will maintain the supply to a piece of equipment in the event of a power failure. At a small scale these are seen attached to computers, giving them enough time to shut down properly. In the industrial work, it may be a generator with an auto-start facility, which may take a couple of minutes to kick in.

In some cases, these two extremes are used together, with enough battery life to last the couple of minutes it takes the generator to get up to speed.

Assorted UPS.

In all of these applications, the choices are varied, but come down to three simple choices. How much power do you need? How long do you need if for? How long can it take to switch over? Even some of the solid state devices use fast relays. There are 'on-line' devices that use an inverter all the time, creating their own voltage and frequency, irrelevant of the incoming live, but beware those UPSs that claim to be 'line-interactive', for they may not be what they seem.

A word of warning: When using a UPS, if the mains power goes and the UPS kicks in, it is easy to forget that the circuit is still live, therefore any installation with this type of back-up should be clearly marked, with warning signs if necessary. Even when switched off, the batteries are often still charged, and an unintentional switch-on (for example due to poor flightcase packing) could have serious consequences.

12.4 International Variations

All around the world, countries have relied on the big powers to help create their power system. There are two main camps: the Europeans, and the Americans. In most cases you will find one of two voltage ranges coming out of the wall.

	UK	Europe (and new UK)		USA
Ground	Green	Green	Yellow	Green
Neutral	Black	Blue		White
Live 1	Red	Brown		Black
Live 2	Yellow	Black		Red
Live 3	Blue	Grey		Blue

Colour Codes.

European: We are now fairly harmonised with the rest of Europe, and the nominal voltage supply is 230v at 50Hz. This means you will get 230 Volts between phase and neutral (and phase and ground) and 400 Volts between phases. This can vary by up to 10% either way, depending whether the country you are in is working its way up from 220V, or, as in the UK, working its way down from 240V. You will find two types of colour codes, the official European, and the traditional UK one.

American: The USA uses a nominal supply of 120V at 60Hz, giving 208 Volts between phases. They frequently use bi-phase supplies for some current hungry domestic loads, such as water heaters, etc. The 'national grid' system in the USA is much more fragmented, as each state set up its own system.

12.5 Multiple Supplies

When you have more than one supply, e.g. two generators, or even two substations, you have to decide how they will interact.

In some cases, you can keep them completely separated and isolated, which in the case of a sound system, is often the best way. However, if you have a generator and a house supply, you may need to tie the earths together to avoid any nasty surprises, as most generators have no reference to ground.

When you have two supplies from different sources, they may not be in phase, and they may not stay in phase if they are. If you start to mix the two, be very careful to make sure they are fixed in relation to both the phase and the voltage. You can 'slave' a generator to the grid, or to another generator, but if you use two supplies 'off the wall', be careful to check where they come from.

13 ADVANCED ISSUES

13.1 Eddy Currents

Eddy Currents are produced when a single-phase cable passes through a metal panel. Magnetic fields are produced that can have adverse effects on the panels themselves, and by inducing current into other cables. Often you will see slots cut in panels between two cables, which is done to prevent the two sets of magnetic fields interacting with each other.

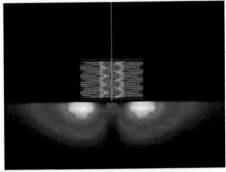

Extreme case showing the disrupted magnetic field of a coil next to a conductive panel.

13.2 Floating Earth / Neutral

A floating earth or neutral is when the connection is either poor or non-existent at the supply end. A poor earth connection could be caused by an earth spike in dry ground, or a floating neutral could simply be a bad connection in the busbar chamber.

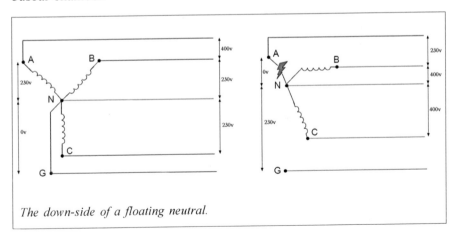

The down-side of a floating neutral.

The result of this is that in the event of a fault, the floating live will be rapidly 'pulled' up to the same voltage as the phase, current will cease to flow, and no fuses will blow. If it is a neutral, this means equipment on the other phases now sees the phase-to-phase voltage. In the case of an earth, the whole distribution system has an earth at mains voltage.

13.3 Induced Earth/Neutral Voltages

What can happen, especially if there is a fault in the system, is that a coil of cable can act as a transformer, 'inducing' a current into an unused line. In normal conditions, when the cable is properly connected at the supply end, this current simply drains away, and you may see a measurement of a volt or two, but not much more. If the induced line is floating, the voltage is rapidly pulled up to line voltage, and if your multimeter has a high enough input impedance, can be measured. If a load (or even your hand) is connected, the impedance to the supply is so high that the voltage is instantly drained away.

So, if when you measure your supply voltages, you see an abnormal reading, use an appropriately rated load (e.g. a light bulb) to determine if you have an induced voltage, which might indicate a floating line, or a fault elsewhere in the building, which may also cause you problems.

13.4 Unbalanced Phases

When you run an imbalanced system, you run the risk of overheating the neutral cable. You are also defeating the objective of using a three-phase supply in the first place.

Phases need to be balanced not just in current, but in type of load as well, inductive, capacitive or resistive.

13.5 Loss of Neutral Under Load

When your system loses its neutral, any imbalances pull the neutral towards the heavier loads. If you are lucky, this reduces the voltage enough to re-balance the load before the lesser-loaded phases are taken up to a voltage where your equipment blows up. If not, and you have no internal protection, you lose two thirds of your system.

13.6 Earth Loop Noise (Hum)

Earth loop noise is every sound engineer's nightmare. This very simple phenomenon is caused by two (or more) paths to earth. The noise is produced

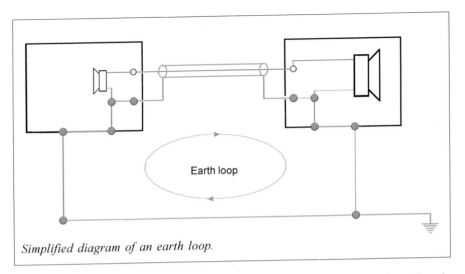

Simplified diagram of an earth loop.

by the electrons trying to reconcile to two (or more) different voltage levels that are trying to establish themselves around the loop.

Any noise on the earth line is rapidly passed around, and is then picked up by every device on the system.

There are some very simple rules to follow:

a) Never disconnect the CPC (Circuit Protective Conductor, or mains earth). This is there to protect your life, has always been there (since the design stage), and is therefore not the source of the problem.

b) Disconnect all the signal lines in turn, until the problem goes away. If it does, you have a device that connects signal ground to mains earth, and that should only happen (at most) in one place. Reconnect everything one connection at a time (leaving out the problem connection) and see if the noise comes back. Some equipment has an earth lift switch on the back. What this should do is disconnect the signal ground from the mains earth, but it might just disconnect the mains earth as well. You have been warned.

c) If all the signal lines are disconnected, and you still have a problem, then you may have a problem with a device being sensitive to the front panel being screwed into a rack with other fittings. Pull it out of the rack and see if the problem goes away. If it does, you may have a device that has to travel in its own case, away from everything else. I would consider this a design flaw and send it back.

13.7 Harmonic Noise

Harmonic noise is produced by loads that modify the waveform in some way. Usually by chopping or consuming current in an un-neighbourly way. We are usually talking about switched mode power supplies and dimmers. Most electronic equipment that is sensitive to this sort of noise should have mains filtering, and in a lot of cases, the sound system will be run off a separate supply to try and minimise the effect.

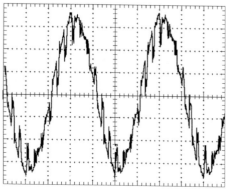

Oscilloscope's view of a harmonically distorted sine wave.

A lot of harmonic noise on the mains lines can be filtered out by a transformer, so if you are a sound engineer on a small tour, packing an isolating transformer can be a worthwhile exercise.

13.8 Surges, Drop-outs and Brown Outs

Every time someone switches on a kettle, it will place an additional load on the supply. When it turns off, it will reduce the load.

Depending where we are in the supply chain, the increased current upstream from us will cause a decrease in the voltage to us. At the end of a line, as in a farm for example, the effect is magnified by every other user on the line.

At the end of a workday, when the factory next door shuts shop, the load decreases and the voltage goes up.

At times, especially when demand is high, or too many power stations are off line, the power companies 'turn down' the live voltage which has the effect (on linear loads anyway) of decreasing the current requirements, reducing the need to get another power station on line. This is called a 'brown-out'.

A 'surge' is a spike of increased voltage on the line. It may be caused by a collapsing magnetic field in a large transformer, or may be what is more commonly called a 'swell' which could be due to a change in power requirements.

A drop out is when all power is momentarily lost, but only for a second or two. This is usually caused by the power company switching the routing of supplies to allow repair or maintenance on a line.

13.9 Switched Mode Power Supplies and Ballasts

When you use a switched mode power supply for a high current application, like an arc lamp, the current waveform becomes much larger, and when the vast majority of lighting equipment on a show could be powered by switched mode supplies, the 100 Amp per phase plus means that your neutral currents can easily exceed

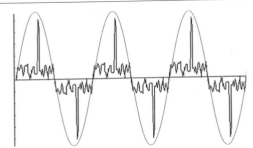

Graph showing sine wave voltage curve, and badly distorted current waveform, produced primarily by the charging of the input capacitors in a switch mode power supply. When added together, very little of the waveform will cancel out.

150 Amps. In order to tell what is going on you need a good quality oscilloscope and current clamp. When you look at the waveform, you will see a series of narrow spikes. On a 250 Watt arc lamp you will find this current spike can be over 10 Amps. Because it is so narrow, none of the phases cancel out, so the neutral current is composed of three sets of spikes per 50 Hz cycle.

If you have 150 luminaires in your system, those peaks could be in excess of 500 Amps. The RMS current of the system will be lower, but will still be higher than the phase current. Remember, if *none* of your phase currents cancel out, your neutral current will be the sum of *all three*.

Many buildings don't even have a fully rated neutral, and here we are looking at having to double rate it. The problems you face may be nothing to do with your cabling. You might be the cause of a transformer fire in the substation, or you may lose the neutral because the wiring gets too hot somewhere in the basement.

13.10 Static

Static electricity is caused by friction. Two surfaces rubbing together can create a charge that will be discharged at the next contact with an earthed object. We all know about walking across carpet, but static can also be produced by the wind blowing tent fabric against a guy-line, which will then discharge as you swing by it on the ground, or by a generator sitting on rubber tyres. Static can be mistaken for a fault in the electrical system, and it is yet another reason for good equipotential bonding on all secondary metalwork.

Again, as with faults on unbonded metalwork, the problem may not always be where it seems.

13.11 Lightning

Under the right circumstances, the potential difference between the earth and the clouds (and sometimes between clouds themselves) becomes so great that an electrical discharge occurs.

Because electricity, in any form, follows Ohm's law, it will seek the path of least resistance. A lightning rod aims to provide the best possible path to ground, in order to protect the structure it is on.

When you start to equipotential bond a large structure such as a scaffolding tower or stage, you may be making it a larger target during a thunderstorm. For this reason, lightning protection is best left in the hands of experts.

13.12 RCDs

Nuisance tripping on RCDs is usually caused by a high level of residual earth current produced by anti-surge and mains suppression devices used in computers and sound equipment. Switched mode power supplies are also a source of earth leakage because of the way they work. When you have a number of such devices in a system, the background (i.e. non-fault condition) leakage can be high enough to trip the RCD. The problem is exacerbated by incorrect application of RCDs in high current situations. Some venues insist on 30mA trips being fitted to 400 Amp supplies, which is ridiculous, and only

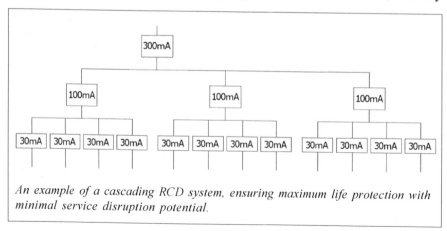

An example of a cascading RCD system, ensuring maximum life protection with minimal service disruption potential.

goes to highlight the misunderstanding of these devices. Even the IEE states that RCDs should not be relied on as primary protection (BS7671: 412-01-01 / 412-06-01). Life protection should be used where and when it is appropriate, and not as a blanket solution.

A good solution is to have a cascading RCD system, where the level of protection is gradually increased throughout the distribution, starting at, say, 300mA/1s on the 400A supply and ending up with 30mA/40ms on the final supply. This should ensure that nuisance tripping does not occur or take out the main breaker and it also offers maximum protection to personnel.

14 CASE STUDIES

14.1 The Case of the Missing Phase

I once got a phone call from the crew at *Miss Saigon*. They were preparing their Vari*Lite system for the day's show, and everything was powering up and calibrating fine. However, as soon as they tried to fire up the discharge lamps, some of their luminaires reset. They looked at the power, metered it, and found no fault. The problem was reproducible, and they could not work out what was going on. All the symptoms were power related, but the power supply was rock solid.

The Vari*Lite system included some VL2 luminaires, which had a minor overheating problem if the line voltage exceeded 245 Volts for any length of time. In the UK, where this could be a problem, a 'bucking' transformer was supplied. This device is an auto-transformer, which has a single coil per phase, on a three-phase core. The transformer was tapped to give a 10% (or 20% if you were unlucky, as this created system problems during brownouts instead) reduction in output voltage.

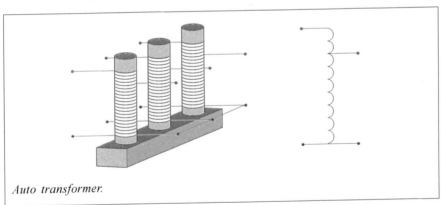

Auto transformer.

When we persuaded the crew to completely disconnect the transformer from the wall (the disconnect was on the output side), they found a phase had blown a fuse. The bucking transformer was generating its own third phase, but it was only about to generate about 10 Amps, which was enough to power the electronics, but not the arc lamps.

This happened because the transformer has a three-phase core, so the magnetic field created by the two good phases was strong enough to create a field in the third winding.

14.2 The Case of the Missing Neutral

In the good old bad days, the Olympia in Paris had a very strange power supply. It had five terminals, one of which was obviously earth. Of the others, there was no marking.

Metering between the four terminals and earth, gave a result of 120 Volts. Four phases? Hardly likely, as metering between the four unmarked terminals gave either approximately 220 Volts or 170V. Most people simply used it as if there were two single-phase supplies with a very dodgy neutral.

What was really going on?

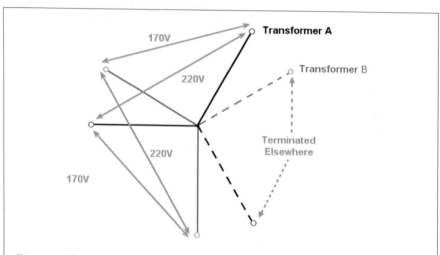

Diagram illustrating the unusal situation of two power supplies in one power outlet box.

The only thing that seems to survive the maths is that there were two supplies in the box, from different substation transformers, which were out of phase with each other. In diagram 44, above, they are shown as 90 degrees out of phase, but we were never able to get to the bottom of it. Since we never trusted the supply, we always recommended a generator. I understand that eventually the venue got a new supply.

14.3 The Case of the Bakery Down the Road

A friend of mine was having a very confusing time. He was working as an IT person (having decided that with at least four if not six children by this point, it was time to get a 'real' job), and the server backups were failing every night. It seemed from the log that the server simply crashed. Every night. Well not quite, only six days a week. Having run all the diagnostics he could, he decided that the only thing to do was to stay overnight. He narrowed down the time to 4:00am with a series of log entries from the system clock.

At the darkest hour, he sat alone in the cold room (air-conditioned because of the servers), and waited. He was rewarded not by some ghostly apparition resetting the server, but by a brownout. Not very long, but long enough. He borrowed a power analyser, recorded a few days' worth of data, and called in the Electricity Board.

They looked into it and traced it to the automatic pre-heat of the ovens in the bakeries down the road. We know they didn't start work until 6:00am, but they had a timer on the ovens to get them up to temperature. Because they all worked off one time switch, there was a massive load suddenly applied to the same 11KV grid the server supply was on.

The Electricity Board persuaded the bakery to install multiple time switches and the problem went away. These days the problem probably wouldn't have been noticed because UPSs are so much cheaper, but at the time, they were the size of a small fridge and cost about the same as the server.

14.4 The Case of the Yellow Ceeform

You may have noticed the usage of the yellow 16A connectors for control purposes on many Lodestar Hoists. This has two problems, the main issue being that 110V is placed on the earth pin, which could be lethal to someone who plugged a 110V power tool into it. As well as that, the use of an IEC 603 connector in control circuitry is disallowed by the standard. It may also be that a 110V power tool with a short to earth could cause unintended movement of a chain hoist, having much larger implications.

Historically, using earth as a return path was an accepted practice for many countries. However, as RCD units have become more of a requirement the world over, I suspect the manufacturers changed the hoist internal wiring to avoid using the earth. As they did not fit the yellow Ceeform as standard, they would have been unaware (and not responsible for) the side effects.

The Health & Safety Executive is now waiting for the industry to move over to an different connection method. They have given us time as long as we recognise the risk in our risk assessments, and take appropriate precautions. A number of rigging companies have taken to making their three pin control cables with special labels, to avoid confusion. At a certain point in the future you will no

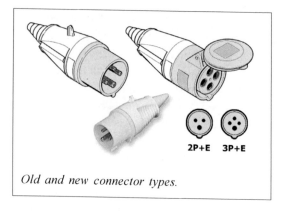

2P+E   3P+E

Old and new connector types.

longer be allowed to use a hoist with the old style connectors, so you have been warned.

It is somewhat amusing to have heard that the UK building industry has been accused of using the 110V centre-tapped power system as a restrictive trade practice to prevent (or make it more difficult) other European companies wanting to work in the UK. As the latest definition of 'low voltage' covers 110V, legally it is as dangerous as a properly maintained 230V system with an RCD. The key element here is 'maintained'. I do not believe that any system that relies on an RCD can ever be called safe without a rigorous testing and maintenance schedule, which is expensive.

14.5 The Case of the Wrong Lamp

The occasional patching error by your local neighbourhood dimmer person is a poor substitute for a real firework display. However, sometimes what you expect to happen, doesn't. Take the situation where, by mistake, a 28v 250W Aircraft Landing (ACL) PAR lamp – which is normally patched as a string of eight lamps in series – is patched instead with a 120v 1000W PAR lamp. At first glance one would think that the lower voltage lamp would blow before the higher, in effect acting as a fuse (assuming that the fuse doesn't actually blow, which it won't unless there is another load on the dimmer channel, and assuming the dimmer channel is fused at 16A or more).

In fact, for two reasons, the 120v lamp blows first. The voltage rating, as mentioned before, is nominal. What really matters is the resistance or impedance of the load. In this case, ignoring any surges, dimmer curves, or anything other than a good, stable, supply; the two lamps in series have different filaments, and therefore the voltage drop across them is not equal. In the diagram, the maths show that the 120v PAR lamp would be subject to 2.7 times its rated value, whereas the 28v ACL is subjected to a lower 2.3 times its rated value. Therefore the 120v PAR is more likely to blow first.

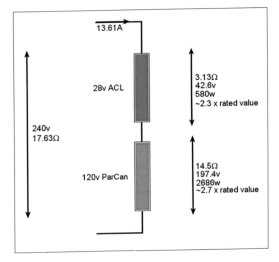

The second reason why the 28v ACL is more robust that the 120v PAR is because it is built for the aircraft industry where everything is build to tolerate peaks of up to 600v. This precaution was partially due to EMF produced by the collapsing magnetic field in relay coils, back in the days when flight control systems had a lot less silicone in them.

15 CURRENT LEGISLATION

15.1 The Management of Health & Safety at Work

The main points in this legislation are to do with the responsibilities of managers (not just the company, but each and every manager, supervisor and self-employed person) to their staff, directly employed or not.

15.2 The Provision and Use of Work Equipment 1998/2306 Regulations (PUWER)

This was revised in conjunction with LOLER in 1998, and covers all equipment used by employees, from a screwdriver to a forklift truck. It replaces many smaller regulations, such as the Abrasive Wheels regulations, and many work-working specific regulations, into a much simpler set. Like so many of the newer regulations, equipment must be safe, fit for purpose, and the staff correctly trained and instructed in its use.

In practice, this means anything from throwing away broken screwdrivers to stop someone doing something unwise with it, to ensure the guards work (and are being used) on a pillar drill.

15.3 Electricity At Work Regulations (EAW) 1989 638

These regulations cover any electrical system, of any age, low voltage, high tension, 12V; anything electrical at all with no exceptions. None. Even your Mag-Lite, and especially your illegally imported cattle prod which has proved so useful in getting the crew out of the tour bus or hotel in the morning.

These are some of the few regulations where there are *absolute* duties and that means the usual 'as far as practicable' doesn't cut it.

In a nutshell, all electrical systems must be designed to prevent danger, maintained to prevent danger, and be operated in a way to prevent danger… These regulations are law, the Wiring Regulations are only a Standard.

If you design, build, operate or maintain electrical equipment within your company or as part or your work duties, this is the ultimate document. This is the document to quote when you want to shut down the lighting rig due to 'unsuitable weather conditions' (Regulation 6).

These are serious regulations. There aren't the usual exclusions for the armed forces, and apart from ships, aircraft and hovercraft (whose captain is ultimately responsible already), the only exclusions are if the HSE gives you one in writing.

PAT (Portable Appliance Testing): As a side issue, many people refer to the 'PAT regulations'. There is no such thing. The regulation that covers PAT is the Electricity at Work regulation 4(2), which is the duty to 'maintain the equipment to prevent danger'. There are other references to maintenance in other legislation, including the Health & Safety Act and the Management of Health & Safety at Work Regulations.

There is a duty to lay out an inspection and maintenance plan, and to record the findings; the rest has been made up by people like the IEE and the PAT equipment manufacturers.

15.4 The Electricity Supply Regulations

Although in theory these regulations only apply to the electrical supply companies, a venue should abide by these, as should a generator supply company. It details, amongst other things, that the supplier should bond the neutral to earth "at or as near as is reasonably practicable to the source of voltage". I read this as the responsibility of the generator supply company in any situation other than a dry hire. Even in a dry hire situation, I would expect them to provide the means to make this bond.

It also covers equipotential earth bonding and provision of a protective earth. It covers how deep or how high cables should be buried or flown, and it covers the legalities of connection two supplies together.

It is also a legal requirement that the supplier tells the customer the number and rotation of phases, the frequency, and the voltage – and the variation the customer can expect. If the variation is not specified, there are default allowances of 1% for frequency and 6% for voltage. The only time this information does not need to be declared is if it is a standard domestic single phase supply of 230V at 50Hz.

15.5 The Electrical Equipment (Safety) Regulations 1994 /32 6
(LVD Directive)

This Statutory Instrument is the UK legislation implementing the EU Low Voltage Directive, which is basically the law that states that anything electrical that runs on 50 to1000V must be safe, and carry a CE mark to prove it.

This UK legislation has not fundamentally changed in a couple of decades, other than to implement the CE mark. It is one of those cases where the law was good enough.

15.6 The Plugs and Sockets, etc. (Safety) Regulations $1994/ 1768$

These regulations primarily cover the use of the 13A plug fitted to consumer/ domestic appliances. It basically says that all these appliances should be fitted when supplied to the end user, with a properly fitted plug, with a fuse of the correct value.

15.7 The Safety Signs Regulations

These Regulations impose requirements in relation to the provision and use of safety signs and signals and implement EU Council Directive 92/58/EEC into UK Legislation on the minimum requirements for the provision of safety and/ or health signs at work.

It covers not only how safety signs should be used, but staff training and implementing the results of risk assessments as well.

15.8 The Electrical Appliance (Colour Code) Regulations

Since these regulations were introduced in 1969, they have been successively amended, and appear to have been completed revoked by The Plugs and Sockets etc. (Safety) Regulations 1994. Cable colour codes are part of BS7671 (aka The IEE Wiring Regs.), and the latest three phase colours are specified in Amendment no2:2004 to BS7671:2001.

15.9 The Electromagnetic Compatibility Regulations $2006/3418$ (EMC Directive)

This Statutory Instrument is the UK legislation implementing the EU EMC Directive, which is the law that states that no two devices can interfere with each other. An issue usually limited to radio frequencies, which is primarily solved by dumping all that nasty RF to earth, where it promptly becomes an earth leakage problem instead. Mains-borne noise is also, of course, a sound engineer's nightmare. What the EMC directive does, very clearly, is lay down a set of rules that means no two devices can interfere with each other in a dangerous way.

It also means that the manufacturer should have tested the device (or the subassembly manufacturer) in such a way that they know how it fails in different situations. From a contractual point of view, if you buy two pieces of equipment, and they interfere with each other, then there are only two things to check: are the emissions too high or is the immunity too low?

There are usually two categories that equipment falls into, Consumer and Industrial. Industrial allows for a higher level of emissions, at the cost of a higher level of immunity. So it is possible to have two items, that are both properly CE marked that interfere with each other, just because the manufacturer chose a different work environment description for the lab. A reputable manufacturer will usually check for the worst of both cases, if there is any doubt, or if the equipment could be classified as 'dual use'.

15.10 The Workplace (Health, Safety and Welfare) Regulations

These regulations cover everything that a toilet needs, from toilets to lighting, access routes to stacking, heating and rest facilities. They cover the basic necessities that an employer is legally bound to provide.

Although of most interest to employers with premises, it is a useful tool in an argument about what should be provided on-site by whom, and I would recommend that all production managers should read it, and add a clause about it into contracts with promoters and venues.

16 CURRENT GUIDELINES

16.1 BS7671
Requirements for Electrical Installations
Prepared by the Institute of Electrical Engineers, this is the leading work on good installation practice; it has no legal status, but compliance is almost always required by contract and local government by-laws (Includes EEC Directives). It is very unlikely that any installation that fully complies with this could be held to not meet the requirements of the Electricity at Work Act 1989.

16.2 BS7909
Design and installation of temporary distribution systems delivering AC electrical supplies for lighting, technical services and other entertainment related purposes.

Covers television, film, theatre, pop concerts and similar events. It aims to bring together in one document guidance on matters of common interest to producing companies, equipment hire companies, events organisers, electrical consultants, electrical installation contractors, service hire companies, equipment manufacturers, venues, and authorities responsible for safety.

16.3 Event Safety Guide
The Event Safety Guide provides guidance to help those who organise music events so that the events run safely by bringing together information needed by events organisers, their contractors and employees to help them satisfy the requirements of the Health and Safety at Work Act 1974 and associated regulations.

16.4 HSE Guidance
There are a number of HSE guidance documents, not only on electrical safety, but on risk assessments and all sorts of other areas. The HSE will tend to avoid specific guidance, but it is quite good at documenting real accidents to serve as training aids and examples.

16.5 BS7697 / HD 472 S1: Nominal Voltages for Low Voltage Public Electricity Supplies
BS7697 :1993 gives the details and timescales for European Harmonisation of

the mains supply. The document was issued in 1993, but the first changes were not introduced until 1995 with a nominal voltage requirement of 230V +10%/-6%, with the date of 1 January 2003 from when all suppliers must generate a nominal voltage of 230V ± 10%, in line with all the other European member states.

What this really means is that our voltage is even move variable than it was before, with a potential range moving from 225.6V - 254.4V (28.8V variance) to 207v-253V (46V variance). Nice to know the government is looking out for us. The net result is that we will all end up buying 230V lamps and wondering why their life at 250V is so short, or why our fridge compressor keeps burning out when it tries to run on 207V instead of 240V. Hurrah for declining standards in the name of harmonisation! The words 'Lowest Common Denominator' come to mind...

17 FURTHER READING

17.1 Fuses

17.1.1 BS 88
Cartridge fuses for voltages up to and including 1000 V AC and 1500 V DC Specification for fuses for use by authorised persons (mainly for industrial application). Additional requirements for fuses with fuse-links for bolted connections.

17.1.2 BS 3036
Specification. Semi-enclosed electric fuses (ratings up to 100 Amperes and 240 Volts to earth).

17.2 Circuit Breakers

17.2.1 BS 3871
Specification for miniature and moulded case circuit breakers. Miniature air-break circuit-breakers for AC circuits.

17.2.2 BS EN 60898
Circuit breakers for over-current protection for household and similar installations. Circuit breakers for AC operation.

17.3 Residual Current Devices

17.4 Cables

17.4.1 BS 5467
Specification for 600/1000 V and 1900/3300 V armoured electric cables having thermosetting insulation. Requirements for construction and methods of test, for cables for use in fixed installations in industrial areas, buildings and similar applications.

17.4.2 BS 6004
Electric cables. PVC insulated, non-armoured cables for voltages up to and including 450/750V, for electric power, lighting and internal wiring.

17.4.3 BS 6007

Electric cables. Single core unsheathed heat resisting cables for voltages up to and including 450/750V, for internal wiring.

17.4.4 BS 6141

Specification for insulated cables and flexible cords for use in high temperature zones.

17.4.5 BS 6207

Mineral insulated cables with a rated voltage not exceeding 750V. Guide to use.

17.4.6 BS 6231

Specification for PVC-insulated cables for switchgear and control gear wiring.

17.4.7 BS 6346

Specification for 600/1000V and 1900/3300V armoured electric cables having PVC insulation.

17.4.8 BS 6500

Electric cables. Flexible cords rated up to 300/500V, for use with appliances and equipment intended for domestic, office and similar environments.

17.4. BS 6724

Specification for 600/1000V and 1900/3300V armoured electric cables having thermosetting insulation and low emission of smoke and corrosive gases when affected by fire.

17.4.10 BS 6883

Elastomer insulated cables for fixed wiring in ships and on mobile and fixed offshore units. Requirements and test methods.

17.4.11 BS 7211

Specification for thermosetting insulated cables (non-armoured) for electric power and lighting with low emission of smoke and corrosive gases when affected by fire.

17.5 Connectors

17.5.1 BS 546 (15 Amp) Abstract

Three-pin plugs and sockets of the round-pin type, as used in domestic premises, offices, etc., for standard ratings of 2, 5, 15 and 30 Amperes. Interchangeability, safety, materials, construction, dimensions. Supplement No. 2 (AMD 5809) gives additional requirements for switched socket-outlets, for use in AC circuits only.

17.5.2 BS EN 60309 ('CeeForm')

Plugs, socket-outlets and couplers for industrial purposes. Dimensional interchangeability requirements for pin and contact-tube accessories.

17.5.3 BS 1363 (13 Amp)

13A plugs, socket-outlets and adaptors. Specification for rewirable and non-rewirable 13A fused plugs.

17.5.4 BS 5550 ('BAC' & 'Lee') (obsolescent).

ENTERTAINMENT TECHNOLOGY PRESS

FREE SUBSCRIPTION SERVICE

Keeping Up To Date with

Eectrical Safety for Live Events

Entertainment Technology titles are continually up-dated, and all major changes and additions are listed in date order in the relevant dedicated area of the publisher's website. Simply go to the front page of www.etnow.com and click on the BOOKS button. From there you can locate the title and be connected through to the latest information and services related to the publication.

The author of the title welcomes comments and suggestions about the book and can be contacted by email at: marco@supporting-role.co.uk

Titles Published by Entertainment Technology Press

ABC of Theatre Jargon *Francis Reid* **£9.95**
This glossary of theatrical terminology explains the common words and phrases that are used in normal conversation between actors, directors, designers, technicians and managers.

Aluminium Structures in the Entertainment Industry *Peter Hind* **£24.95**
Aluminium Structures in the Entertainment Industry aims to educate the reader in all aspects of the design and safe usage of temporary and permanent aluminium structures specific to the entertainment industry – such as roof structures, PA towers, temporary staging, etc.

Basics - A Beginner's Guide to Stage Lighting *Peter Coleman* **£9.95**
This title does what it says: it introduces newcomers to the world of stage lighting. It will not teach the reader the art of lighting design, but will teach beginners much about the 'nuts and bolts' of stage lighting.

Basics - A Beginner's Guide to Stage Sound *Peter Coleman* **£9.95**
This title does what it says: it introduces newcomers to the world of stage sound. It will not teach the reader the art of sound design, but will teach beginners much about the 'nuts and bolts' of stage lighting.

A Comparative Study of Crowd Behaviour at Two Major Music Events *Chris Kemp, Iain Hill, Mick Upton* **£7.95**
A compilation of the findings of reports made at two major live music concerts, and in particular crowd behaviour, which is followed from ingress to egress.

Electrical Safety for Live Events *Marco van Beek* **£16.95** ISBN: 1904031285
This title covers electrical safety regulations and good pracitise pertinent to the entertainment industries and includes some basic electrical theory as well as clarifying the "do's and don't's" of working with electricity.

The Exeter Theatre Fire *David Anderson* **£24.95**
This title is a fascinating insight into the events that led up to the disaster at the Theatre Royal, Exeter, on the night of September 5th 1887. The book details what went wrong, and the lessons that were learned from the event.

Health and Safety Aspects in the Live Music Industry *Chris Kemp, Iain Hill* **£30.00**
This title includes chapters on various safety aspects of live event production and is written by specialists in their particular areas of expertise.

Hearing the Light *Francis Reid* **£24.95**
This highly enjoyable memoir delves deeply into the theatricality of the industry. The author's almost fanatical interest in opera, his formative period as lighting designer at Glyndebourne and his experiences as a theatre administrator, writer and teacher make for a broad and unique background.

Focus on Lighting Technology *Richard Cadena* **£17.95**
This concise work unravels the mechanics behind modern performance lighting and appeals to designers and technicians alike. Packed with clear, easy-to-read diagrams, the book provides excellent explanations behind the technology of performance lighting.

An Introduction to Rigging in the Entertainment Industry *Chris Higgs* **£24.95**
This book is a practical guide to rigging techniques and practices and also thoroughly covers

safety issues and discusses the implications of working within recommended guidelines and regulations.

Let There be Light - Entertainment Lighting Software Pioneers in Interview
Robert Bell **£32.00**
Robert Bell interviews an assortment of software engineers working on entertainment lighting products.

Lighting for Roméo and Juliette *John Offord* **£26.95**
John Offord describes the making of the production from the lighting designer's viewpoint - taking the story through from the point where director Jürgen Flimm made his decision not to use scenery or sets and simply employ the expertise of Patrick Woodroffe.

Lighting Systems for TV Studios *Nick Mobsby* **£35.00**
Lighting Systems for TV Studios is the first book written specifically on the subject and is set to become the 'standard' resource work for the sector as it covers all elements of system design – rigging, ventilation, electrical as well as the more obvious controls, dimmers and luminaires.

Lighting Techniques for Theatre-in-the-Round *Jackie Staines* **£24.95**
Lighting Techniques for Theatre-in-the-Round is a unique reference source for those working on lighting design for theatre-in-the-round for the first time. It is the first title to be published specifically on the subject, it also provides some anecdotes and ideas for more challenging shows, and attempts to blow away some of the myths surrounding lighting in this format.

Lighting the Stage *Francis Reid* **£14.95**
Lighting the Stage discusses the human relationships involved in lighting design – both between people, and between these people and technology. The book is written from a highly personal viewpoint and its 'thinking aloud' approach is one that Francis Reid has used in his writings over the past 30 years.

Pages From Stages *Anthony Field* **£17.95**
Anthony Field explores the changing style of theatres including interior design, exterior design, ticket and seat prices, and levels of service, while questioning whether the theatre still exists as a place of entertainment for regular theatre-goers.

Practical Guide to Health and Safety in the Entertainment Industry
Marco van Beek **£14.95**
This book is designed to provide a practical approach to Health and Safety within the Live Entertainment and Event industry. It gives industry-pertinent examples, and seeks to break down the myths surrounding Health and Safety.

Production Management *Joe Aveline* **£17.95**
Joe Aveline's book is an in-depth guide to the role of the Production Manager, and includes real-life practical examples and 'Aveline's Fables' – anecdotes of his experiences with real messages behind them.

Rigging for Entertainment: Regulations and Practice *Chris Higgs* **£19.95**
Continuing where he left off with his highly successful *An Introduction to Rigging in the Entertainment Industry*, Chris Higgs' new book covers the regulations and use of equipment in greater detail.

Rock Solid Ethernet *Wayne Howell* **£24.95**
Although aimed specifically at specifiers, installers and users of entertainment industry systems, this book will give the reader a thorough grounding in all aspects of computer networks, whatever industry they may work in. The inclusion of historical and technical 'sidebars' in this book makes for an enjoyable as well as informative read.

Sixty Years of Light Work *Fred Bentham* **£26.95**
This title is an autobiography of one of the great names behind the development of modern stage lighting equipment and techniques.

Sound for the Stage *Patrick Finelli* **£24.95**
Patrick Finelli's thorough manual covering all aspects of live and recorded sound for performance is a complete training course for anyone interested in working in the field of stage sound, and is a must for any student of sound.

Stage Lighting for Theatre Designers *Nigel Morgan* **£17.95**
An updated second edition of this popular book for students of theatre design outlining all the techniques of stage lighting design.

Technical Marketing Techniques *David Brooks, Andy Collier, Steve Norman* **£24.95**
Technical Marketing is a novel concept, recently defined and elaborated by the authors of this book, with business-to-business companies competing in fast developing technical product sectors.

Theatre Engineering and Stage Machinery *Toshiro Ogawa* **£30.00**
Theatre Engineering and Stage Machinery is a unique reference work covering every aspect of theatrical machinery and stage technology in global terms.

Theatre Lighting in the Age of Gas *Terence Rees* **£24.95**
Entertainment Technology Press is delighted to be republishing this valuable historic work previously produced by the Society for Theatre Research in 1978. *Theatre Lighting in the Age of Gas* investigates the technological and artistic achievements of theatre lighting engineers from the 1700s to the late Victorian period.

Walt Disney Concert Hall *Patricia MacKay & Richard Pilbrow* **£28.95**
Spanning the 16-year history of the design and construction of the Walt Disney Concert Hall, this book provides a fresh and detailed, behind the scenes story of the design and technology from a variety of viewpoints. This is the first book to reveal the "process" of the design of a concert hall.

Model National Standard Conditions *ABTT/DSA/LGLA* **£20.00**
These *Model National Standard Conditions* covers operational matters and complement *The Technical Standards for Places of Entertainment*, which describes the physical requirements for building and maintaining entertainment premises.

Technical Standards for Places of Entertainment *ABTT/DSA* **£30.00**
Technical Standards for Places of Entertainment details the necessary physical standards required for entertainment venues.

Go to www.etbooks.co.uk for full details of above titles and secure online ordering facilities.